TO CREATE
A MODERN
AGRICULTURE

To Create
a Modern
Agriculture

Organization and Planning

A. T. Mosher

Agricultural Development Council, Inc.
630 Fifth Avenue, New York, N.Y.   10020

Published in the United States of America in 1971 by
The Agricultural Development Council, Inc.
630 Fifth Ave., New York, N. Y. 10020

Library of Congress Catalog Card Number: 70-182038
Printed in the United States of America by Sowers Printing Company
Lebanon, Pennsylvania

PREFACE

This book grew out of an invitation to the author to deliver a series of three Lal Bahadur Shastri Memorial Lectures at the Indian Agricultural Research Institute, New Delhi, in February 1971.

An early draft of the lectures was circulated for criticism to all members of the professional staff of the Agricultural Development Council, and to about ten other consultants. The final draft of the lectures in the form in which they were delivered was discussed at the conclusion of each lecture and became the basis for seminars in the Philippines, Indonesia, Malaysia, and the State of Mysore in India.

Participating in those seminars were members of planning commissions, directors of departments of agriculture, directors of research in universities, consultants provided by technical assistance agencies, university graduate students, and administrators of a wide variety of governmental agencies related to agriculture.

The version of the lectures now being published has been prepared subsequent to these various discussions in Asia. It has seemed better not to adhere to the three-lecture format but to reorganize the material partly to increase readability and partly to take advantage of the criticisms that emerged from the discussions.

The major reactions to the lectures were not the ones the author had anticipated. He had expected strong criticisms by planners more devoted to econometric methods of planning. There were only a few of these. The dominant reactions to the planning procedures proposed were twofold. Some commentators seemed to be earnestly seeking to find a meaningful way to plan for agriculture without having found one. They did not hastily agree that the proposals made here are the answer, but they seemed to welcome a set of definite proposals that might point in a useful direction. The other widespread reaction came from persons who had already concluded that a pragmatic "project" approach is the only workable one. In general, they felt that the proposals made in the lectures presented a more systematic way of pursuing an approach to which they were already committed.

As for the proposals with respect to organization of public activities related to agriculture, the positive reaction was that here was a definite way to integrate planning, budgeting and implementation. The major negative reactions were of two types. It was frequently pointed out that the author had presented a "normative" model, an ideal toward which a government might try to move but could not be expected to reach because of bureaucratic rigidities and jealousies. The other criticism had to do with the degree of simplicity/complexity of the proposed form of organization. Critics in some countries felt it called for more well-trained administrators than are available. Other critics argued that a more complex set of organizations is needed.

All of the criticisms received were helpful to the author. All of them have been taken into account in revising the manuscript, even though, frequently being in conflict with each other, they could not all be accommodated.

I wish to express my gratitude to all of the many persons who have contributed to this book by their criticisms and discussions of various parts of it. They have kept me from many errors and brought additional insights to bear on the topic.

I wish to thank particularly Dr. M. S. Swaminathan, Director, and Dr. Kissen Kanungo, Dean of the Graduate School, Indian Agricultural Research Institute, for the invitation that made it possible to prepare the manuscript and present it for critical discussion.

Even after much revision, taking specific criticisms into account, the book must remain one person's interpretation of how best to deal with an important and complex problem.

A. T. MOSHER

New York
October 1971

CONTENTS

ix

INTRODUCTION

Our topic is organizing and planning to create a modern agriculture.

One reason for selecting this theme might be that it would be considered important by Shri Lal Bahadur Shastri, in whose memory these lectures were established. He was concerned about the quality of life of the millions of people living in India's villages, and during the years when he was Prime Minister he urged that government services be improved in order to meet the country's needs more adequately.

Another, and perhaps a better, reason is that we stand at a point in the process of agricultural development when a reconsideration of forms of governmental organization and of agricultural planning is particularly timely.

Present forms of organization of public agencies throughout South and Southeast Asia stem from three origins. Some of them are part of a colonial heritage. Others represent borrowings from other countries since independence, partly in the drafting of new constitutions and partly under the influence of external technical assistance agencies. Still others are innovations that have been introduced, country by country, to cope with some particular aspect of agricultural need, whether for credit, or community development, or a prices commission, or to administer land development and settlement, or some other. Many of these special purpose organizations have been set up outside of ministries of agriculture, thus dispersing authority with respect to important aspects of agricultural development.

During the same period that these organizational borrowings and innovations were occurring, national planning began to be adopted in different forms in different countries. It usually began as overall national economic planning. It included attention to agriculture, but in a form dictated more by the need to treat agriculture as one sector among several in the process of macro-economic planning than in a form internally appropriate to the nature of agriculture itself. In most cases, the planning was done by a central planning agency, with the ministry of agriculture playing only a minor role, if any at all.

Despite these developments, agricultural productivity did not improve appreciably until the new high-yielding varieties of certain major cereals became available in 1964. Then agricultural productivity increased very rapidly in certain places. Two interesting developments followed. One was the rather embarrassing discovery, in Pakistan, for example, that wheat production had spurted far ahead of what the provisions made by the Plan for increased farm inputs would have made possible. After the fact, it was found that the installation of thousands of private tube wells, utilizing pumps and diesel engines manufactured locally and completely outside of the Plan had been a major factor. We have been accustomed to planned production targets not being met and have blamed implementation. But when targets are surpassed it raises questions about the extent to which planning itself is even pertinent. The other development following the advent of the "Green Revolution" was that the increased productivity highlighted the inadequacy of many existing marketing and credit agencies to do their tasks, and that has led to renewed interest in forms of organization.

It is in this context that it seems particularly pertinent, in 1971, to reexamine both the organization of public agencies and planning related to agriculture. Organization and planning should be considered jointly because the issues involved in both are so closely intertwined: organization of public activities is part of what needs to be planned, and good planning depends in part on appropriate organization both for planning itself and for implementation of the Plan.

There is still another reason for believing that the time is ripe for a reconsideration of these matters. I am convinced that the time has come when we should reformulate our *objective* in agricultural development. All of us, I believe, have been so intent on securing whatever agricultural growth we could immediately that we have not thought far enough ahead. Seldom have we considered what, ultimately, we would like to achieve in agriculture. Perhaps there was an excuse for that in the past but not now. Recent rapid rises in productivity in certain regions have demonstrated that a drastically different and more productive agriculture is actually possible in many parts of South and Southeast Asia. I believe we should now raise our sights, take stock of what will need to be accomplished in order for that to be achieved, and organize and plan toward that end.

I would define our new objective as being *to create a modern agriculture* over as much of each country as possible. Some forms of organization and planning are pertinent in the period before the setting of such an objective was worthwhile; they are outmoded. Others will be pertinent after a modern agriculture has been achieved, but not before; we are trying to use some of them already and they are ineffective for current tasks. Our task today is to design forms of organization and planning that are particularly suited for use *during* that period when setting the objective of creating a modern agriculture has become realistic and timely but during which the objective has not yet been reached. It is that task to which I wish to direct attention by making some concrete proposals about how it might be done.

What is a modern agriculture? It is one in which:

1. the technology and efficiency of farming are continuously being improved;
2. the kinds of commodities produced on farms are constantly changing (at least in their proportions to each other) in response to changing market demands and costs of production;
3. the quality of land, the competence of labor, and the forms and quality of capital instruments used in farming are steadily being improved;
4. the proportions in which land, labor and capital are combined in farming keep changing in response to changes in population growth rates, changes in alternative employment opportunities, and changes in farm technology as expressed in shifting relative prices of factors of production;
5. finally, and this gets at the heart of our task, a modern agriculture is one that is served by private and public agencies that are continuously being adapted to serve new functions in new ways.

A modern agriculture can take any one of many forms, but it is always changing. There is no specific crop variety; no particular form of farm organization; no fixed relationship in the proportions in which land, labor, and capital are combined; no particular land or tax or price policies; no immutable form of governmental organization that singly or together constitute a modern agriculture. Instead, a modern agriculture is one that is highly dynamic and highly flexible, as well as increasingly productive.

A modern agriculture may or may not be highly mechanized, although there is always a tendency for it to move in that direction. Japan had a modern agriculture by my definition long before tractors began to be used to any appreciable extent.

Part I

BASIC CONSIDERATIONS

There are certain basic considerations that must be taken into account in both organization and planning of public activities related to agricultural development.

One of these is the distinctive characteristics of agriculture as an industry.

Another is the major functions that public agricultural activities should perform.

A third is the necessity of adopting parallel categories for both organization and planning in order that there may be effective linkages between planning, budgeting and implementation.

It is these three basic considerations that are discussed in chapters 1, 2 and 3.

1

Chapter 1

CHARACTERISTICS OF AGRICULTURE AS AN INDUSTRY

Let us begin by reminding ourselves of several well-known characteristics of agriculture as an industry that should be taken into account in organizing and planning to create a modern agriculture.

A BIOLOGICAL PRODUCTION PROCESS

First, agriculture is an industry characterized by a particular production process—one which directly utilizes solar energy through the biological growth processes of plants and animals. Unlike the steel industry, the shoe industry, the textile industry, each of which produces a particular commodity, agriculture produces a wide variety of commodities. Because of the current widespread need for more food there is a tendency to equate agriculture with food production. But agriculture produces fibers, industrial oils, leather, rubber, and other products as well. It is its biological production process that sets agriculture apart as a separate industry, rather than the nature of its products.

One of the cardinal principles of good agricultural planning flows directly from this characteristic. It is that the primary goal of public activities related to agriculture is to increase the profitable opportunities to utilize the unique production process of agriculture in each set of local circumstances throughout a country, almost regardless of what specific products each region produces so long as there is an economic demand for them, at home or abroad. Much too frequently we think of the agriculture of a country as being made up of so many million acres of rice, wheat, cotton, groundnuts, oil seed crops, etc., and so many head of various classes of livestock. Instead, in designing patterns for the organization of public agricultural agencies and for planning it is more useful to think of the agriculture of a country as being made up of thousands or millions of *farm businesses* of various sizes and types, each attempting to utilize the biological production process of agriculture profitably. The present cropping pattern in any country is always a reflection of what has been most profitable in the past, given certain family needs and the market demand for different products. Those needs and opportunities change over time with changes in technology, in market demand, and in access to markets at home and abroad. Consequently, we should not assume that each region will produce its present set of farm products indefinitely. We should concentrate instead on creating and maintaining a flexibility of each agricultural region to shift from crop to crop as technological and economic conditions change.

Farming Ranges from Subsistence to Commercial

Second, the farms of most countries vary enormously in the extent to which each produces for family consumption or for sale in the market at the present time. This fact complicates the task of securing agricultural growth. Most methods of increasing farm productivity involve the use of purchased inputs, and those farms near the subsistence end of the continuum from subsistence to commercial produce little cash income out of which inputs can be bought. More importantly, subsistence farming creates a particular mentality or outlook (what Penny,[1] working in Indonesia, called "subsistence-mindedness") that makes such farmers resist becoming involved in market operations. Many of them are very reluctant to shift from growing cereals to producing other products primarily for the market because they do not want to put their families' food supply in jeopardy by having to buy it at uncertain prices. Even when some of their products are sold, a great many farmers still determine their cropping patterns primarily from the standpoint of family needs and market only each year's surplus.

To participate in a modern agriculture it is necessary *either* that each farm move toward the commercial end of the continuum *or* that farmers who produce only or primarily for home consumption have some off-farm employment that produces cash income out of which farm inputs can be financed. The first of these is the more likely route. However, the second has been extremely important in Japan and recent studies show it to be happening now in Pakistan. This second alternative needs to be seriously considered in many countries, not instead of trying to make many farms more commercial but in addition to it. In countries with limited land and a large rural labor force, part-time farming needs to be analyzed for its potential role as part of an overall strategy.[2]

Four Functional Components of a Modern Agriculture

The third characteristic of agriculture that has marked implications for organization and planning is that, in its modern form, it has four essential functional components, only one of which is farming itself.

In a subsistence agriculture "farming" and "agriculture" are synonymous; each farmer uses only his own land and family

---

[1] D. H. Penny, "The Transition from Subsistence to Commercial Family Farming in North Sumatra" (unpublished Ph.D. dissertation, Cornell University, 1964).

[2] One approach to this is the recent study by Professor Wyn Owen, "Two Rural Sectors: Their Characteristics and Roles in the Development Process," Occasional Paper, International Development Research Center (Bloomington, Ind.: Indiana University, 1971).

labor. In a modern agriculture farming is still central, but each farm becomes only the assembly line, utilizing and combining many different types of inputs drawn from throughout the economy.

Some of those inputs are provided by *commercial agri-support activities* that comprise the second functional component of agriculture. These include the manufacture and distribution of farm inputs, marketing and processing services to handle farm products, and credit to finance farming operations. They are called *commercial* agri-support activities because farmers normally pay for them as they are used, whether they are provided by the private sector or by governmental agencies.[3]

The third functional component of a modern agriculture is made up of *non-commercial agri-support activities*—services that farmers need but that they typically do not pay for directly. Agricultural research is one of these; education and training of farmers and of the technicians who operate agri-support services is the other.

Agri-support activities, both commercial and non-commercial, are not farming, but they are essential off-farm components of a modern agricultural industry. If a country had no farms it would not need agri-support activities.

The fourth functional component of the agricultural industry is what might be called the *agri-milieu*.[4] It is a combination of all of the influences that affect what can be done within farming and agri-support activities, but that are general to the whole country.

Some of these influences are economic:

1. the state of domestic industry, and the consequent domestic demand for farm products;

---

[3] A note on public and private commercial agri-support activities is to be found in Appendix A, p. 139.

[4] The Report of the U.S. President's Science Advisory Committee entitled *The World Food Problem* (Washington, D.C.: The White House, May 1967), called this the "agri-climate." Many people have criticized that term on the grounds that it will normally be thought to refer to the natural phenomena of climate and weather. Dr. Richard P. Momsen, of the Inter-American Institute of Agricultural Sciences, has suggested using the term "agri-milieu" instead.

6

2. the extent of non-agricultural employment opportunities;
3. price and tax policies;
4. foreign trade opportunities;
5. domestic income distribution;
6. general transportation facilities; and
7. the rate of population growth.

Another part of the agri-milieu is made up of political factors:

1. land tenure policies;
2. general development policies;
3. agricultural development policies; and
4. the extent of farmers' participation in the political process.

Still other aspects of the agri-milieu are cultural:

1. the traditions and values of the people;
2. the structure of the society; and
3. the extent of general education.

All of these taken together form a general environment of opportunities, constraints, inducements and attitudes that set *the rules-of-the-game* within which farming and agri-support activities must be conducted. They are not formulated primarily for their impact on agriculture, yet they need constantly to be scrutinized. It is important to see just what effects they are having on agriculture, in order to determine what changes might be advisable. Even though its many aspects are not overtly agricultural, therefore, it is important to count the agri-milieu as one of the four functional components of an agricultural industry, along with farm businesses, and with commercial and non-commercial agri-support activities.[5]

What is the relevance of this discussion of the four functional components of a modern agriculture for organization and planning? It is that each of them requires specific but differing types

---

[5] For a more extended discussion of the functional components of agriculture, see "What is Agriculture?", *The World Food Problem, op. cit.*, Vol. I, pp. 60-73.

FARMING

AGRI-MILIEU

POLITICAL

ECONOMIC

CULTURAL

NON-COMMERCIAL

COMMERCIAL

AGRI-SUPPORT

FARMERS' PARTICI-
PATION ON POLITICAL
PROCESSES

POLICIES ON:
LAND TENURE
PRICES & TAXES
AGRIC. DEV.

FARM BUSINESSES

TRANSPORTATION
FOREIGN TRADE
DOMESTIC INDUSTRIES
& SERVICES

TRADITIONS & VALUES
SOCIAL STRUCTURE
GENERAL EDUCATION

PRODUCTION & DISTRIBUTION
OF FARM INPUTS, MARKETING,
PROCESSING, AND DISTRIBUTION
OF FARM PRODUCTS

PRODUCTION CREDIT FOR FARMERS

RESEARCH
EXTENSION
TRAINING OF
AGRICULTURAL
TECHNICIANS

**Functional Components of a
Modern Agriculture**

of public attention. Sometimes it is a changed public policy that is needed. Sometimes it is a public program. Sometimes it is public stimulation and/or regulation of activities in the private sector. *Basically, the task of public organization and planning is to assure an adequate and appropriate development of agri-support activities, both commercial and non-commercial, and to achieve appropriate changes in the agri-milieu.*

THE GEOGRAPHIC STRUCTURE OF AGRICULTURE

The fourth characteristic of agriculture that is of great importance in creating a modern agriculture is its geographic structure.

We are accustomed to the fact that farms must be widely dispersed throughout a country in order to take advantage of sunlight and appropriate soils where they are available. It is also important to realize that agri-support activities must be made equally widely available. To accomplish that, two units of geographic organization are crucial. One is the *farming locality*. The other is the *farming district*.

A farming locality is the area within which farmers can easily travel to a locality center, avail themselves of all of the agri-support services they need there and get home again within a reasonable period of time on the same day. The locality market center should provide:

1. a local market for farm products;
2. retail outlets for all needed farm supplies and equipment;
3. services of an extension agent;[6]
4. production credit; and
5. access roads between farms and the locality's market town where all of these services are available.
6. Somewhere nearby there needs to be, in addition, a set of local verification trials to determine the most profitable farm practices for the locality.

---

[6] Whether or not there is an extension agent for each locality should depend on the density of population and size of farms. Normally, one extension agent would serve more than one locality.

9

(Effective farming localities can be of different sizes depending on prevailing methods of travel and transportation. Where many farmers must travel on foot or by cart, a locality market center cannot effectively serve farmers more than four to five miles away.)

A *farming district* is the area within which the *farming localities* it embraces can be adequately serviced from a district headquarters. Such a district headquarters should contain facilities for servicing each of the agri-support activities carried on in its locality market centers. In addition, it should have adequate roads to connect all locality centers with the district headquarters and to connect the district headquarters with the outside world.

Again, there is no universal criterion as to the size of an effective farming district. In general, a district headquarters can adequately service localities whose market centers are within about twenty-five miles of it, assuming that roads on which trucks can travel connect all of the locality market centers.

This geographic structure of a modern agriculture is of great importance and is frequently neglected. In arranging for rural agri-support services, the places at which these are made available are usually too far apart. As a result, many farmers are much too far away from the supplies and services they need. Many village market towns provide one or two components of an effective farming locality but not the others. Yet the complementarity among all six components is so great that one or two are of little value without the others. Markets for farm products and locally available supplies and equipment are the absolute minimum. An extension service, locally available production credit, and verification trials can increase the rapidity with which farmers adopt new technology. Adequate roads to tie farms and agri-support services together become increasingly important as market sales increase, as more purchased inputs are used, and as fields are occupied by crops more months of each year.[7]

---

[7] The availability of consumer goods and of facilities for depositing savings make a locality center even more valuable to farmers in the surrounding countryside.

Because of the high complementarity among agri-support activities and the dependence of farming localities on district support, *farming districts are the most efficient unit for expansion of agri-support activities.*[8]

REGIONAL VARIATIONS

The fifth characteristic of agriculture that should have a profound impact on organization and planning is that it is subject to great variation from region to region within each country.

Differences in production possibilities. The initial source of this geographic variation is differences in soils, climate and topography that make different regions best suited to rice, wheat, maize or sugarcane; to rubber, tea, coffee or coconuts; or to livestock. Terracing and irrigation modify the natural factors of topography and rainfall that lead to regional differences, but these are present in some places and not in others, thus leading to further regional variations.

Apart from natural differences in soils and climate, geographic variations in agricultural production are induced by differences in the location of each region with respect to major urban industrial centers and access to foreign markets. The growth of each city increases the demand for certain perishable farm products and thus encourages production of them nearby. Regions with easy access to seaports have a cost advantage in producing for export. Obviously, the availability and efficiency of transport facilities have a major influence. Regions distant from a city can provide it with perishable products if economical transportation is dependably available. Similarly, regions far inland can produce for export if transportation is available and cheap. Thus market and cost factors, as well as natural factors, influence the almost infinite

---

[8] For a more extended treatment of the geographic structure of agriculture, see, A. T. Mosher, *Creating a Progressive Rural Structure* (New York: Agricultural Development Council, 1969), chapters 1, 2 and 3.

A more general background treatise on this topic is E. A. J. Johnson, *The Organization of Space in Developing Countries* (Cambridge, Mass.: Harvard University Press, 1970).

variations that characterize agricultural production in different regions of each country.

Differences in potential for growth. Still other factors come into play with respect to the potential of different regions within a country for agricultural growth. One is the availability of new technology tested and ready for use. In the past few years, regions growing wheat, rice and maize have forged ahead while regions growing most other crops have not. Similarly, the presence or absence of irrigation facilities that allow precise water management practices makes some regions more ready for rapid agricultural growth than others.

These regional variations in readiness for rapid agricultural growth are of the utmost importance in planning to create a modern agriculture. They dictate which parts of each country can achieve a modern agriculture quickly, and in which places particular preliminary activities must be completed first. They will be discussed more fully in the next chapter.

INTERDEPENDENCE OF AGRICULTURAL AND INDUSTRIAL DEVELOPMENT

A sixth characteristic of a modern agriculture is that it is interdependent with industrial development. Agricultural development requires an increasing economic demand for its products. To some extent, expanded farm production can flow through international trade to meet economic demand in other countries. For the most part, however, the demand for farm products depends on domestic industrial development that increases the number of productively employed non-farm workers who buy their food, and through domestic industries that utilize farm products as raw materials. Furthermore, an advancing agriculture needs supplies and equipment that are industrial products: fertilizers, pesticides, tools and implements, fuels and building materials.

Conversely, unless agriculture is being developed and rural incomes are rising, there is an inadequate domestic demand for

12

industrial products, particularly in countries where most of the population is rural. Many countries have expanded certain types of industrial production capacity prematurely, before there was an adequate demand for their products.

A simultaneous development of agriculture and non-farm industry benefits both.

AGRICULTURE: PRIVATE AND PUBLIC

One final characteristic of agriculture that has enormous consequences for organization and planning is that many of the decisions and actions that affect agricultural growth and rural welfare are private—taken by individuals and private business firms within a country—while many others must be public—taken in legislative halls and executive agencies of the government.

The exact division between what is done privately and what through public action varies from country to country. The general situation can be expressed in four statements, each referring to one of the four functional components of a modern agriculture.

1. The management of farm businesses is generally private.
2. The agri-milieu can be modified only by public action.
3. Non-commercial agri-support services must be publicly managed.
4. Commercial agri-support activities can be either private or public, with great care taken in either case to avoid monopoly or to regulate monopoly where it is unavoidable.

The important point is that public organization and planning should be appropriate to the most effective combination of public and private agricultural activities. It should give particular attention to modifying the agri-milieu in ways that allow farm businesses and all agri-support services to operate efficiently. It should assure ample and effective agricultural research services, see to the education and training of agricultural technicians, and operate an effective extension service. With respect to commercial agri-support services, it should at least establish business standards, market grades, laws governing contracts and loans with regulatory

13

agencies and courts to enforce them. It may, in addition, find it advantageous to operate one or more commercial agri-support services directly in certain circumstances, although in general these are more efficient when privately operated. It should leave the planning of actual farm production to farm operators.

Sometimes what public policy *allows* is more important than what it *regulates*. We have all heard the comment, "What government can do to speed development is to get out of the way!" Although that is only half true, it *is* half true. We need types of organization and planning both to set men free and to discipline their joint efforts. When we recognize that a progressive agriculture is always partially private and partially public we are saying also that agricultural growth depends partly on what men do individually (for which they need freedom and a wealth of alternative opportunities, among which they are free to choose with a minimum of regulation) and partly on what they do jointly through the agencies of their government and through voluntary forms of cooperation.

SUMMARY: THE UNIQUENESS AND COMPLEXITY OF AGRICULTURE

It is the characteristics of agriculture reviewed in this chapter that should be the base on which we build in discussing organization and planning to create a modern agriculture.

Agriculture is an industry based on a unique production process, drawing its energy from the sun and utilizing that energy through the biological growth processes of plants and animals. It can and does produce many different products. It takes many economic forms varying all the way from purely subsistence to highly commercial farming.

A modern agriculture is an industry having four functional components: (1) farm businesses within which agricultural production takes place; (2) commercial agri-support activities that provide farmers with the supplies, equipment and credit they need and that market, transport and process farm products; (3) non-commercial agri-support activities of research and education for farmers and for agricultural technicians; and (4) an agri-

14

milieu of legal arrangements, price arrangements, tax and monetary policies, development policies, and social values that are conducive to agricultural growth.

A modern agriculture requires a definite geographic organization providing fully functioning farming *localities* that place every farmer within easy reach of all the facilities he needs, and farming *districts* each of which meets the needs of the farming localities within it.

There are important geographic variations both in production possibilities and in readiness for agricultural growth that need to be taken into account in encouraging agricultural growth and in improving rural welfare.

Those interested in agricultural development must also be concerned about industrial development because of the interdependence between the two.

Activities and responsibilities related to agriculture are partly private and partly public. Public organization and planning should take both types into account.

Chapter 2

AGRICULTURAL PRODUCTION, GROWTH AND ADJUSTMENT

Our concern throughout this book is the organization and planning of public activities and policies during that period when creating a modern agriculture is a feasible goal but has not yet been widely achieved. However, public activities and policies must pay attention to other concerns with respect to agriculture as well, during that same period. Organization and planning must make provision for them also.

Public activities and policies play three roles with respect to agriculture:

1. they are part of the *production process* of agriculture, even at a constant level of production;
2. they should contribute to agricultural *growth*;
3. they should contribute to *adjustment* within agriculture and between agriculture and other sectors of the economy.

PUBLIC PARTS OF AGRICULTURAL PRODUCTION

Although farming itself is generally private, certain essential public activities are really part of the agricultural production process: market information services, establishing and policing

manufacturing an automobile in that it involves the simultaneous construction of a number of highly complementary parts. In designing an automobile attention must be given to designing and constructing very dissimilar components, each of which serves a particular essential purpose: an engine block, a carburetor, a generator, a muffler, tires, comfortable seating, and a protective body. Each of these is quite different from the others; and the proportionality and complimentarities among them are far more important than any cost/benefit analysis of individual components. Similarly, a modern agriculture is made up of units of biological research, manufacturing plants for fertilizers, farm-to-market roads, arrangements for periodically revising public policies, farm credit, and a number of other components no one of which can substitute for any of the others and each of which can only contribute to agricultural production when combined with the others. Most, but not all, elements of the structure of a modern agriculture are not commodity specific. They can serve equally well in the production of wheat, cotton, vegetables, sugarcane, or any other crop.

Both of these types of activities aimed at agricultural growth are important. Both need to be provided for in the organization and operation of a ministry of agriculture. Activities to increase the utilization of present capacity make the most of present opportunities; those to build the structure of a modern agriculture expand opportunities for the future. The first without the second at best delays ultimately needed improvements in the basic structural elements of a modern agriculture; at worst it results in a considerable lag of current capacity behind current technological potential. The second without the first results in considerable and persistent lags of current production behind current capacity. Keeping both precisely in balance is impossible, but working on both simultaneously is both feasible and economical.

Throughout this book preponderant attention is given to building the *structure* for a modern agriculture. That is because in our urgency to increase production we have slighted the structural transformation within agriculture that is essential if a truly modern agriculture is to emerge. Such neglect may have been justifiable in the past, but both the problems and the opportunities induced by the new high yielding varieties of major cereals have demonstrated that a truly modern agriculture can now be created in many parts of most countries of south and southeast Asia. But not everywhere! One of the dangers we now face is that of wasting resources by trying quickly to create a modern agriculture *throughout* each country. That cannot be done. Instead, it is important to tailor programs to the widely differing needs of different parts of each country.

The key to that differentiation is the varying growth potential of different areas.

Adjusting Programs to the Differing Growth Potentials of Different Parts of a Country

To adjust agricultural programs to differing growth potentials two steps are needed. One is to classify the lands of the country on the basis of the immediacy of their potential for agricultural growth. The other is to specify the types of programs that should receive priority in each type of region.

Land Classification by Growth Potential

What is needed is a tripartite classification, based on a realistic judgment as to when or whether each part of the country has the potential to become an area of truly modern agriculture—dynamic, flexible, and highly productive.

Each country in South and Southeast Asia has substantial areas of *immediate* growth potential (IGP Areas): areas of agricultural land on which rapid agricultural growth is possible within the next three years. These are areas: (1) where growing conditions of soil, climate, and water availability are favorable; (2) where new technologies are already available that promise substantially higher production of at least one major crop now being grown; and (3) now having efficient transport links with the national economy. It is in such areas—and *only* there—that a truly modern

21

agriculture can be created (if it does not already exist) within a period of a few years.

Each country has other substantial areas of agricultural land that have a *future* growth potential (FGP Areas). These are areas having favorable conditions of soil and climate but where one or more of the other essential elements of an area of immediate growth potential is presently lacking. Such an area may lack adequate water supplies and control for higher production, or it may lack new technology to allow higher production of major crops now being grown (or that could be grown) in the area, or it may lack transportation access to tie it into the national economy. To provide the missing element or elements will require time. Whether the need be the construction of irrigation and drainage facilities, or crop research, or providing major highway access, the process will require several years before higher production becomes possible. Consequently, while such areas may have a high potential for future agricultural growth, that potential cannot begin to be realized for several years to come.

In addition, each country has other areas (in which a largely subsistence type of farming may now be widespread) that have a *low* potential for agricultural growth as far into the future as we can now see (LGP Areas). For them to have a potential for agricultural growth will require one or more major technological breakthroughs that we cannot confidently predict at the present time. These are most likely to be areas of low moisture availability for substantial parts of each year, and where no economic source of irrigation water is available, either surface or subsurface, or where the topography is quite rough.[9]

It should be emphasized that classifying agricultural lands on the basis of their potential for agricultural growth does not mean classifying whole farming districts as units in this manner. Few farming districts in any country lie wholly within one or another of these classes. Instead, a basic requirement for sound agricul-

---

[9] For a more extended treatment of this method of defining regions having different growth potentials, see *Creating a Progressive Rural Structure, op. cit.,* pp. 54-74, and 96-106.

tural planning is to classify the lands *within* each farming district as to the immediacy of their potential for agricultural growth.

TAILORING PROGRAMS TO GROWTH POTENTIAL

Once such a classification has been completed (and it should be revised annually as circumstances change) appropriate program elements can be combined into a plan for the development of each area over the next few years.

The objective should be to give *appropriate* attention to *all* of the territory within each district. That requires that program proposals be tailored to the immediate needs and feasibilities within each type of area. (See chart on page 25.)

IGP Areas. It is the areas of immediate growth potential, and those only, that are ready for public efforts to increase the production of specific farm commodities, to provide a complete Progressive Rural Structure,[10] and to complete the creation of a modern agriculture. Meanwhile, research to find additional new technologies relevant to these areas should be continued, as should projects of land development that can further increase the potential for additional agricultural growth.

FGP Areas. In areas of future agricultural growth potential, priority should be given for the time being to activities that will lift them to the category of areas of immediate growth potential: research to find new technologies for crop or livestock production for which such areas are suited; or the construction of feasible irrigation or drainage facilities; or the construction of a main highway to tie each such area into the national economy. Until whichever of these activities that may be needed are completed it

---

[10] "Progressive Rural Structure" is the designation given by the author in an earlier publication (*Creating a Progressive Rural Structure, op. cit.*) to a comprehensive rural agri-support infrastructure consisting of markets for farm products, retail outlets for farm inputs, production credit, extension services, local verification trials, and farm-to-market roads to serve each farming locality and district. It is the "rural circulatory system" of a modern agriculture and is discussed more fully on pages 33 and 34.

would be uneconomic to proceed with the other activities to accelerate agricultural growth for which IGP Areas are now ready.[11]

LGP Areas. In areas of low (agricultural) growth potential it is useless to make public expenditures to encourage *agricultural* growth since we see no grounds for optimism that such growth can occur. However, any feasible ways to develop non-farm employment should be encouraged. In addition, the people now farming in such areas deserve public services that will at least give them or their children mobility to move elsewhere and that will, meanwhile, help them achieve as good a life as possible where they now are. Schools, health facilities, major highways between larger towns and cities, and selected community development activities are the most important instruments for this.

It may be inferred from this listing of the activities appropriate to areas having differing potentials for agricultural growth that I am suggesting that more public resources be spent in IGP Areas than in areas with lower potential. Such an inference would be a mistake. This classification of agricultural land and the tailoring of public activities to it is equally valid regardless of what policy may be adopted with respect to giving greater attention to more productive areas or to the most needy areas. What the classification does is to make it easier to adjust programs to regional differences, and in doing that to assure that the activities emphasized in each area will be *those for which each type of area is ready and from which it can benefit.*

It is the welfare of people about which we should be concerned, not the productivity of land *per se*. But what can be done *through agriculture* in any particular place does depend on the characteristics and location of the land and on the geographic location of appropriate public services. For this reason, agricultural planning must give great emphasis to different agricultural

---

[11] Providing a skeleton Progressive Rural Structure that ties market centers of farming "localities" to district headquarters is worthwhile in FGP Areas, but not farm-to-market roads.

Tailoring Programs to Differing Potential for Agricultural Growth

Lands of Immediate High Potential for Agricultural Growth (IGP Areas)	Lands of Future High Potential for Agricultural Growth (FGP Areas)	Lands of Low Potential for Agricultural Growth (LGP Areas)
Commodity-Oriented Projects		
Complete Progressive Rural Structure		
Skeleton Progressive Rural Structure		
Land Development		
Regional Research		
Programs to Promote Rural Welfare and Non-Agricultural Employment		

regions and in doing that the potential for agricultural growth of each part of the country is critical.

It is only as those responsible for planning within each district realistically classify its agricultural land on the basis of growth potential that they can propose a plan which will make the most effective use of whatever resources are available.

Promoting Agricultural Adjustment

The third objective of public activities related to agriculture, in addition to participating in production and promoting growth, is to promote agricultural adjustment. One form that the need for adjustment takes, even quite early in agricultural development, is the need for attention to income distribution as between farmers. Typically, increases in agricultural production occur commodity by commodity. Those farmers growing the commodity for which a more profitable technology becomes available forge ahead while the others lag behind.

Another type of adjustment that is frequently needed is to weigh the advantage of higher prices to farmers against the advantage of lower farm prices to urban consumers and make whatever adjustments seem indicated.

Still another type of adjustment that should continuously be considered is between agriculture and other parts of the economy. At one stage it may be advantageous to encourage a net flow of capital into agriculture to expand its capacity, while at other times it may be advisable to encourage a net flow in the other direction. After industrialization begins to pull labor out of agriculture, or as the non-farm demand for staple foods becomes less elastic and commercial export opportunities are limited, it may even be in a country's interest to shift resources out of agriculture and let agricultural production decline in order to concentrate on other more profitable opportunities.

The need for agricultural adjustment takes many forms, but whatever form it takes it calls for one or more types of public action.

26

SUMMARY

The point of this discussion of production, growth, and adjustment is not that different activities of a ministry of agriculture are related solely to one or another of these three objectives. They are not. The same activity may serve two, or all three, depending partly on how much of it is undertaken, how it is conducted, and where within the country it is concentrated. It is important that the three objectives be kept in mind, however, lest the people of a country fool themselves about what is being done for agriculture. A ministry could have a very substantial budget with all of its expenditures devoted to current production and no investment being made in growth. Conversely, substantial investments may be made to spur growth, but be limited in their returns because inadequate attention is being devoted to those activities that are really the public part of agricultural production. Or problems of adjustment may be ignored only to build up social or economic crises for the future.

Agricultural organization and planning should take all three of these functions into account. Too frequently development plans are drawn up that provide only for investments or "development expenditures." They provide only for public expenditures in addition to the established on-going activities of each ministry, but do not critically review the need for the non-development expenditures that support those already established. Many plans are not consistent about this, however. They sometimes budget development funds for subsidies that help pay for increased current production without laying any base for continuing higher production.

The principle to be drawn from this discussion is that agricultural planning should embrace all public programs related to agriculture whether their purpose be current agricultural production, agricultural growth, or adjustment.

Chapter 3

ESTABLISHING PARALLEL CATEGORIES
FOR PLANNING, BUDGETING
AND IMPLEMENTATION

W hether one is considering organization or planning,[12] a major problem that must be faced is how to classify the various activities for which provision must be made.

CRITERIA IN CHOOSING TYPE OF CLASSIFICATION

The classification chosen needs to satisfy several criteria.

First, it must be a classification that is consistent with the characteristics of agriculture as an industry. Some existing forms of organization of public activities related to agriculture do reflect

---

[12] The term "planning" has a narrower connotation in this book than many planners prefer to give it. Many planners argue that planning includes implementation. They insist that planning means systematic activity in pursuit of explicitly defined objectives, and thus set up a sequential determination of, first, "objectives," then "intermediate goals," then program or policy "instruments," then "projects" and the implementation of those projects.

Others prefer a simpler sequence that they define as "plan formulation" (in terms of broad macro-economic categories); programming (for individual sectors of an economy); and implementation. In terms of this classification, what I choose to call (agricultural) planning is quite similar to what is meant, by others, by "programming."

I prefer not to include implementation as part of planning. To me, planning is what is done *in preparation for* action. The action that follows then constitutes "implementation."

particular needs within agriculture, but others appear to reflect classical academic organization into "disciplines," and few have been designed specifically to fit the peculiarities of agriculture as an *industry* made up of many types of widely dispersed farm businesses embodying many different combinations of crop and livestock enterprises, serviced through farming localities and combining both private and public production activities.

Second, it needs to be appropriate for *action*. This means that it needs to separate from each other those activities that are inherently different, that require different kinds of professional competence, that require different kinds of administration. By the same token, it needs to group together in the same category those activities that are similar in the above respects. It needs also to group together those activities that are so highly complementary in their dependence on each other that to separate them leads to unnecessary difficulties of coordination.

Third, the classification needs to be such that it can be used for both organization and planning. If it does not meet this criterion, it becomes very difficult to translate a plan into action. If planning proceeds without specifying which agency is to do what or, worse still, if a single item in a plan can simultaneously be claimed for implementation by several agencies, the result is either agency bickering, or failure to achieve implementation, or both. Many experts in planning have urged that "planning, budgeting and implementation must be integrated." If they are not, what is done in the budgeting process will become the effective plan and what was done at the planning stage will be largely disregarded. Using identical categories for planning and for agencies of implementation can alleviate this difficulty.

Fourth, the classification selected must take account of all three of the functions of public activities related to agriculture: participation in agricultural production, promotion of growth, and agricultural adjustment. The cost of all of these must be met from public funds. How much can be spent on one is influenced by how much is spent on the others. Consequently, all need to be considered together in the planning process.

Fifth, despite what has just been said the classification needs to be one in which priority is given to its usefulness in promoting agricultural *growth*. It may bear repeating that our concern in this discussion is solely with that period *during which* creating a modern agriculture is a possibility and a major objective. It is with countries that have some areas of immediate growth potential, some of future growth potential, and some of low (agricultural) growth potential as defined in Chapter 2—countries that have many farms that are becoming increasingly commercial as well as many that are still close to the subsistence end of the continuum—countries that have substantial areas where further improvement of the land itself is still possible. This situation characterizes most of the countries of South and Southeast Asia.

Considerations of participation in agricultural production and of influencing agricultural adjustment are important even in this period, but whenever there is a conflict between the organizational and planning needs of these two functions and those of the function of accelerating agricultural growth, it is the need for forms appropriate for promoting agricultural growth that should prevail.

A RECOMMENDED CLASSIFICATION

Taking into account all of these criteria, and making adjustments among them where necessary, I conclude that we should adopt six major categories for both organization and planning:

1. agricultural research;
2. assuring adequate wholesale supplies of farm inputs;
3. developing a rural infrastructure of agri-support services, or, as I have called it elsewhere, a "progressive rural structure";
4. giving appropriate attention to farmers' incentives and agricultural prices;
5. improving agricultural land through irrigation and other appropriate means; and
6. undertaking or strengthening arrangements for educating and training agricultural manpower.

Agricultural research. We begin with the fact that a modern agriculture, whatever else it may demand, requires a continuously improving technology for farm production and for marketing products. That leads immediately to the first major element: *Research.*

Each country needs a national agricultural research system, with many different kinds of component parts. For the most part it must be publicly financed research, since most farms are too small to conduct their own research and because it is almost impossible for those conducting research directly to recoup their necessarily high costs, except in large agri-business corporations with wide markets and frequently with brand-name products.[13] Moreover, some of the research needed is specifically to inform public policy-making, and for this there is no "consumer" except the government.

The publicly supported research that is needed runs the gamut of crop and livestock breeding and management, farm business management, pest and disease control, problems of marketing, storing, and transporting farm products, developing effective farm inputs, problems of pricing both inputs and products, projecting the demand for and supply of individual farm commodities, the economic impact of land tenancy systems, and many others.

Some types of research can best be conducted in well-equipped and staffed central research stations; others require on-the-site experimentation in individual type-of-farming areas.

It is important that some research be conducted by each college or university that is training agricultural technicians, partly to assure that those who are teaching be learners as well, and partly in order that students may become acquainted with the methods of doing research.

All of these kinds of research and types of research organizations need to be articulated into a national system of agricultural research—not necessarily a single monolithic research organization (which could not, in any case, encompass the privately

---

13 See T. W. Schultz, *Transforming Traditional Agriculture* (New Haven: Yale University Press, 1964), p. 150.

financed research of agri-business corporations) but certainly through one or another type of coordinated approach. National coordinated research programs on particular crops, as in India, have demonstrated the possibility of collaboration among a wide variety of research organizations.

Research is an important activity even with respect to agricultural production, apart from growth, because of its importance in keeping ahead of new plant and animal diseases and to facilitate appropriate changes made desirable by changing product and input prices. But its greatest importance is in building the technological base for agricultural growth and in identifying institutional changes that would be beneficial. That importance flows partly from the fact that growth depends on new technology and new institutional arrangements, and partly from the fact that the availability of new technology induces many other types of development on which productive use of the new technology depends by increasing private and public demands for them.[14]

Assuring adequate wholesale supplies of farm inputs. But the results of research provide only a *potential.* Before they can be utilized many of them must be embodied in physical supplies and equipment: new seeds, fertilizers, pesticides, implements, etc. Producing these involves very different processes from those of research. It involves the multiplication of seeds and the industrial manufacture of the other farm inputs. Alternatively, it requires the importation of farm supplies and equipment from other countries. In either case it requires making estimates of probable aggregate needs, and warehousing and financing activities.

Developing a rural infrastructure of agri-support services. The fact that agricultural production must take place on farms that are widely dispersed wherever sunlight and suitable soils, moisture, and temperature are available means that it is peculiarly dependent on an equally widespread network of agri-support ser-

[14] Yujiro Hayami and Vernon W. Ruttan, *Agricultural Development: An International Perspective* (Baltimore: Johns Hopkins University Press, 1971).

vices. It is these services that make available to farmers in each farming locality the materials, information, training and credit that they need in order to produce up to the limit set by the technology available from research activities and by prevailing local prices.

As stated in Chapter 2, this Progressive Rural Structure is made up of six elements to be made available in each farming locality:

1. retail outlets for farm supplies and equipment;
2. markets for farm products;
3. an agricultural extension service;
4. production credit for farmers;
5. local verification trials;
6. farm-to-market roads, and roads connecting each farming locality center to district headquarters.

Each of these agri-support activities involves different processes, and requires a different type of organization and administration, but what they have in common is that *jointly* they meet the need for a rural "circulatory system" to provide farms with the materials, ideas, and financing they must have if they are to participate in a modern agriculture, and to take their products to market. Jointly they provide the geographic structure of a modern agriculture. The complementarity among them is so strong that extending them to additional districts, and to localities in areas of immediate growth potential, needs to be closely integrated. It is this high complementarity that leads to grouping them together as a single element for purposes of organization and planning.

Production incentives for farmers. Even having adequate agri-support services available in a locality will not result in farmers using them unless they have adequate incentives to do so.

Farmers' incentives are affected by the availability of production inputs; they are affected by the adequacy of the Progressive Rural Structure; they are affected by what is done about land development; they are affected by general tax, fiscal and mone-

34

tary policies; they are affected by relative prices and by land tenure practices.

There are three distinct kinds of activity with respect to incentives that require attention.

The first is the investigational task of keeping informed about the current situation with respect to farmers' incentives in major agricultural regions. This involves studies of costs of production and local prices in different parts of the country, estimates of demand and of supply response, studies of the impact of different tenure systems and other economic as well as technological factors.

The second requirement is also investigational. It consists of devising changes in policies with respect to prices, subsidies, or land tenancy that could improve the situation. It also includes designating areas in which provision of a Progressive Rural Structure should be accelerated or its operations improved.

Third, if direct subsidies of farm input prices, guaranteed market prices for selected farm commodities, or crop insurance schemes are undertaken, administrative arrangements must be made to implement them. A separate bureau may be required for administering each of these, but it is important that all such activities be kept together under one coordinating agency so that the bearing of all investigational and administrative activities on each other and on farmers' incentives can be honored and exploited. Similarly, in planning, attention to farmers' incentives must receive explicit and major attention.

Land development and management. So far, the activities provided for are those that make it possible to apply better technology on the land, but the quality of the land itself for agricultural production is also subject to improvement through irrigation, drainage, land clearing and land shaping. This again is quite a different type of activity, involving primarily engineering operations, but requiring extensive agronomic and economic studies as well if the projects undertaken are to lead to maximum production opportunities.

35

While public construction and land development are the activities (within this category) most obviously bearing on agricultural growth, the quality of *management* of irrigation systems also affects opportunities for increasing production, as does the management of public lands.

Here, again, separate bureaus may be required for different activities within the category, but all of them need to be seen as a unit in both organization and planning.

Education and training of agricultural technicians. Certainly one of the major impediments to rapid agricultural growth in many countries is the lack of adequately trained personnel to operate the wide variety of agri-support activities, both public and private, that a modern agriculture requires: research; the manufacture and distribution of production inputs; making farm credit widely available in appropriate forms; the marketing, storage, transportation and processing of farm products; the training of farmers to utilize new technologies; and the task of teaching itself, to develop all of the skills and types of understanding that are needed.

To speak of the need for technical manpower training is *not* identical with considering the programs of schools and colleges alone. Schools and colleges can do important parts of what is needed, but they are not the best environment for developing many of the skills and types of understanding required in particular agri-support activities. Many of those can be developed much more rapidly and effectively on the job or in intermittent brief periods of in-service training. Moreover, in a developing economy the types of skills that are most needed keep changing, so no matter how pertinent school and college curricula may be much of what they teach is outmoded within five to ten years, but individual careers last twenty-five to forty years.

All efforts to educate and train agricultural technicians need to be treated as one unit: schools, colleges, pre-induction and in-service training. That is partly because what one type of training does not accomplish others must, and partly because agricultural colleges and universities are frequently the best agencies to conduct certain types of in-service training.

Summary

The categories proposed in this chapter have been chosen, as was stated earlier, to achieve a classification of public activities that: (1) is appropriate to the characteristics of agriculture as an industry; (2) separates activities that are inherently different but groups together those that are most highly complementary; (3) is appropriate for use in both organization and planning; (4) takes account of all three functions of public activities (participation in agricultural production, promoting agricultural growth, and contributing to adjustment); and (5) gives priority to the need for agricultural growth and for creating a modern agriculture.

In the chapters that follow, suggestions are made as to how this classification can be used in organizing public activities related to agriculture, and in agricultural planning.

Organization will be considered first because strengthening each essential agency is part of what needs to be planned, and because each agency should play an appropriate role in the process of planning itself.

Part II

ORGANIZING TO CREATE A MODERN AGRICULTURE

"The really tough part of economic development is not fabricating improved technologies but rather the organizational tasks of recombining human behavior under new rules that enable people to help each other in creating and putting to widespread use the more effective technologies.

"Unlike physical materials and forces, the rules that combine behaviors into mutually helpful ways of living and making a living are not lifeless affairs. They are very much alive because, at least, the most important ones are interlocked with deep-seated convictions (beliefs) which people hold concerning the kinds of rules which deserve their respect and allegiance, and the kinds that merit their distrust and opposition. . . .

"Economic development is thus far more than a mere technological or physical transformation of inputs into increasing outputs, it is more fundamentally an organizational transformation

of old ways of life and work into new rules of interpersonal be-
haviors. And this in turn is possible only to the extent that people
are able to make revisions in their heritage of basic convictions
concerning the kinds of interpersonal rules which do and do not
deserve their respect and support."[15]

---

[15] Joint Commission on Rural Reconstruction, "Agricultural Development and Its Contribution to Economic Growth on Taiwan," *Economic Digest,* Series No. 17, Taipei (April 1966).

Chapter 4

GENERAL CONSIDERATIONS AND PRINCIPLES

For the most part, attention to organization has been given to significant but separate parts of the problem of organizing to promote agricultural growth. The problems of reorganizing patterns of land ownership and tenure has received much attention, as has the reorganization of farms through consolidation of holdings. Numerous arrangements have been devised for extending credit to farmers, for marketing farm products, and for distributing farm inputs. Many attempts have been made to get farmers to enter into new forms of organized group action.

Less attention has been given to reorganizing existing governmental programs into a more effective pattern, and least attention of all to reorganizing ministries of agriculture. In fact, the prevailing tendency has been to move away from the problem by setting up independent agricultural agencies outside of the ministry in order to bypass its shortcomings and inefficiencies, rather than frontally to attack the problem of reorganizing the ministry itself to make it more effective.

Let us examine another approach. Let us assume that some

government, somewhere, were to decide to look afresh at the task of organizing its agricultural activities. Let us assume that it decides the time has come when creating a modern agriculture should be a primary concern. Under these circumstances what should be the function of its national ministry of agriculture? How should the ministry be organized? And what should be the mechanisms for reconciling and coordinating its activities and responsibilities with those of other ministries of the government?

It would be unrealistic for us to presume that any pattern we might devise would quickly be established. It would likewise be folly to contend that every country should organize its public agricultural activities in the same way. But let us try to determine what one effective form for such organization might be *during that period when creating a modern agriculture is the primary objective.* At a later time another form is almost certain to be preferable; the need for change and flexibility in governmental organization is as important as in any other phase of a dynamic society.

ARBITRARY DOMAINS OF MINISTRIES

Let us begin by recognizing that there is no conceivable way to organize a government so that the division of functions and responsibilities among ministries is not to some extent arbitrary. The responsibilities of different ministries are bound to overlap to a degree. What each of them does has repeated repercussions on the central concerns of other ministries.

For example, a minister of education can logically argue that his ministry should be responsible for all vocational education, including that offered in agricultural colleges, while a minister of agriculture can equally well argue that since technical agricultural training is involved, and since increasing the number of well-trained agricultural technicians is an important element in agricultural growth, overseeing agricultural education should be a responsibility of his ministry. Whichever ministry gets the administrative responsibility, what it does will affect what the other ministry is interested in. A minister of trade can make a strong case for his ministry being responsible for stimulating expansion of export crops, while the minister of agriculture can contend that his ministry should decide on public activities with respect to all types of agricultural production, whether for domestic or foreign trade. A minister of public works can logically hold that secondary feeder roads as well as main highways, and the location of both, are matters for his ministry to decide, while the minister of agriculture may with equal logic maintain that his ministry is in a better position to determine the location of rural feeder roads and should have a major say about the location of main highways in agricultural regions as well.

One consequence of this situation is that there is no hope, nor would it be wise to try, to accommodate all of the activities that impinge on agriculture in one way or another in a ministry of agriculture. Instead, what should be done is to try to group within the ministry of agriculture all of those activities that have to do *primarily* with agriculture, and then establish effective means of interaction with other ministries whose activities impinge on agriculture in various ways.

HISTORICAL PRECEDENTS, POLITICAL OPPORTUNISM, AND LOGICAL ORGANIZATION

Along with recognizing that any conceivable organization of a government into ministries is to some extent arbitrary, it is important also to understand how particular existing patterns of organization for a ministry of agriculture come into being.

Almost every country has a ministry of agriculture with a minister of cabinet rank, although one country in Southeast Asia has only an Undersecretary for Agriculture within a Department of Agriculture and Natural Resources. However, there is enormous variation in the scope of activities for which existing ministries of agriculture have responsibility. Some have responsibility for irrigation, others do not. Some have responsibility for agricultural education, others do not. Some have responsibility for the management of state-owned agricultural estates, others do not. Some have responsibility for land settlement and/or for public agricultural credit agencies, some do not.

Some of these differences are to be accounted for by historical precedents going back to varying patterns of colonial government, or to differences in borrowings from patterns of administration of other countries when new constitutions were drafted. Other differences are due to political opportunism. In some cases, the responsibilities of a ministry have been divided to make two or more ministries available to be headed by deserving political leaders. In other cases, ministries have been consolidated to give wider authority to a particular minister. In still other cases, specific responsibilities have been removed from a ministry and given to independent agencies responsible directly to the prime minister or president, either to indicate their importance or to bypass cumbersome established processes within ministries.

The point here is not that any one of these politically or administratively inspired changes constitutes an unwise decision under appropriate conditions. Rather, it is that in many cases existing forms of organization have *not* grown out of a logical assignment of responsibilities in line with problems of agricultural production, growth and adjustment. Instead, they are strongly influenced by historical precedents and political opportunism. Moreover, forms of organization, once established, tend to continue long after the reasons that gave birth to them have lost their validity. This is true of patterns borrowed from a colonial heritage from the very beginning. It is true of changes adopted in order to give power to, or remove it from, a particular administrator as soon as he is transferred or defeated in an election.

We say, repeatedly and accurately, that institutional change is basic to development. However, established governmental agencies and universities are among the most difficult institutions to change, even though they may view their function as one of "agents of change." Change others? Yes. Change themselves? Seldom.

With the foregoing complications in mind, let us now consider what a reasonable and effective organizational structure for a ministry of agriculture might be. We shall do this in two ways. In this chapter we shall list some major characteristics that such an organizational structure should have. The next chapter will outline a form of organization that would embody those characteristics.

DESIRABLE CHARACTERISTICS OF ORGANIZATION OF A MINISTRY OF AGRICULTURE

1. *The organization of a ministry of agriculture should make provision for contributions to agricultural production, growth, and adjustment with a primary emphasis on growth.*

At all stages of agricultural development a ministry of agriculture should make provision for all three of these objectives. But in the present era in Asia, the paramount need is rapid agricultural growth, and to build and improve the structure of a modern agriculture. Not only are all countries in this part of the world dominantly agricultural now but the absolute number of persons dependent on cultivation for a livelihood cannot be reduced within the next twenty-five to thirty years. Even the most heroic efforts to industrialize cannot increase non-farm employment as rapidly as the population of working age is bound to increase within that period. Consequently, while due regard must be given to maintaining and expanding those public activities that are part of agricultural production, and provision will need to be made for promoting certain forms of agricultural adjustment that become urgent, the overriding objective in organizing a ministry of agriculture must be to achieve a form of organization that responds efficiently to the need for agricultural *growth* and for creating a modern agriculture as rapidly as possible.

2. *A ministry should be so organized that planning, budgeting and implementation utilize identical categories.*

It is a corollary of the requirement just discussed that major organizational units within a ministry of agriculture should be parallel to the major components of *planning* for agricultural growth. One hears all too frequently the complaint that planning tends to be done by a planning commission, budgeting is largely controlled by the ministry of finance, and responsibility for imple-

45

mentation falls to ministerial or non-ministerial agencies whose stated roles are not defined in a manner that makes them wholly and solely responsible for each of the activities necessary to implement specific parts of the plan. That criticism, put another way, is that the *categories* of planning, budgeting, and implementation are not the same. To correct that fault, where it is present, one step that needs to be taken is to organize the ministry of agriculture in such a way that it has separate bureaus, departments or agencies for implementing each of the major components in terms of which planning for agricultural growth should be done, along lines suggested in the previous chapter. Another is to organize the ministry in such a way that its several units can participate in the planning process in appropriate ways. If those steps are taken, then planning, budgeting and implementation with respect to agriculture can move forward in a mutually reinforcing manner.

3. *The organization of a ministry of agriculture should provide for the administration of some programs, and for gathering information and making analyses relevant to others.*

The first of these requirements is the most obvious. To a considerable degree, a ministry is an implementing agency: it puts policies into practice by administering activities relevant to its responsibilities. But since many of the policies and activities that affect agriculture lie within the domains of other ministries, the organization of a ministry of agriculture needs to include provision for keeping track of how the policies and programs of other ministries are affecting agriculture, so that appropriate consultations can be initiated and agriculture's representatives in those consultations can be well-informed.

The need for staff work related to responsibilities of other agencies is particularly strong with respect to development planning. Where a planning commission virtually monopolizes the planning process in isolation, a frequent reason is that ministries (including agriculture) have little or no planning competence. If agriculture wishes to be heard in planning, its ministry must equip itself, through its organization and procedures, to participate with competence.

But it is not just the activities of other ministries and other governmental agencies about which a ministry of agriculture needs to be organized to keep itself informed. It needs also to be organized in such a way as to keep posted on what the private sector is doing, particularly with respect to commercial agri-support activities, in order to make valid decisions about what, if anything, the government should do. And, of course, an adequate statistical service with respect to farm production itself is essential, and usually it is up to the ministry of agriculture to operate it.

4. *A ministry of agriculture should be structured to administer appropriate national activities, not attempting to exercise inappropriate control over activities that should be left to regional or local administration.*

There can be no inflexible rules about precisely which agricultural activities should be nationally administered and which should be directed regionally or locally. Only general guidelines are possible. Efforts to affect the agri-milieu by changing tax or price policies usually must be made at the national level. It is always wise to have a national research system, although there should be regionally dispersed research facilities, and these may or may not be regionally administered within a cooperative framework for the system as a whole.

Planning the program of an agricultural extension service, on the other hand, is best done locally or for very small regions because of wide variations in production problems. But even where program planning is done locally, regional or national activities are essential for in-service training, for extension publications and other publicity materials, and to provide subject-matter specialists.

In between these two extremes are many activities that may be nationally, regionally, or locally administered, depending on the size of the country and on circumstances within each country.

The general principle, however, is universal: organization of a national ministry of agriculture should provide for *appropriate* national activities, and not aim at uniform national administration of specific activities except in those cases in which that is clearly essential.

5. *A ministry of agriculture should be organized so as to stimulate and conduct differentiated development programs, region by region.*

One of the biggest mistakes commonly made in pursuit of agricultural growth is to sponsor uniform programs over an entire country without taking into account substantial differences in the immediacy of the potential for agricultural growth, region by region.

To argue for regional differentiation of programs is *not* to propose that government resources be concentrated either (1) where they will have the largest and quickest payoff in increased production, or (2) where farm families currently are in the greatest need. Instead, it is to argue for launching and improving, in each region, those types of activities which are most needed and most likely to be productive at the present stage of development of each. It is wasteful to establish uniform programs throughout a country, without taking into account the current greatest needs of each region; and the organization of the ministry of agriculture should be such as to facilitate such regional variations, particularly to correspond to varying growth potentials, as discussed in Chapter 2.

6. *A ministry should be so organized and administered as to provide a balance between autonomy and coordination of each of its divisions, bureaus or other agencies.*

As we come, in the next chapter, to suggest a form of organization for a ministry of agriculture, it will become clear that the activities which a ministry must administer are extremely diverse. Conducting agricultural research is quite different from operating an agricultural statistical service. Running a credit program is quite different from supervising an extension service, and that in turn is very different from administering a price subsidy program.

The consequence is that many different types of administration are called for by the activities that different bureaus or divisions of a ministry of agriculture must undertake. The only way to achieve these differences effectively is by giving a large measure of autonomy to the head of each bureau, division, or agency within the ministry.

But the differing needs of various activities that call for a large measure of administrative independence do not obviate the equal need for a reasonable degree of coordination. There is a high degree of interdependence among all agricultural agencies in what they do, and competition among them for available resources. The interdependence must be honored and the competition resolved by adequate coordination.

Consequently, the organization and administration of a ministry of agriculture needs to be such as to strike a balance that combines wide operating autonomy for each of its agencies with effective overall coordination.

7. *A ministry of agriculture should be so organized that it can contribute to an optimum adjustment of various interrelationships between agriculture and other sectors of the economy and between producers and consumers of farm products.*

The ministry of agriculture is one of a team of ministries that together are responsible for public activities related to the whole economy and the welfare of all the people. What is to be avoided is the emergence of an adversary relationship among ministries with each becoming a special pleader for a particular industry or for a particular kind of governmental activity. Consequently, the ministry of agriculture should be so organized that it can keep in touch with a whole set of intersectoral relationships, in which agriculture is one element, and help make appropriate adjustments in them.

One of the important interrelationships that must constantly be assessed and appropriate adjustments made is that between

"The mistakes made as a result of delegating authority are less costly than the stultifying effects of centralized decision-making."

Utilizing different types of administration. Another of the requirements of creative administration is to recognize that each of the proposed divisions and many individual bureaus require a distinctive type of administration. Some agencies need a type of administration that primarily centralizes control or monitoring of inventories (as in a Division of Production Inputs) or of financial accounts (as in a Bureau of Farm Credit). Some need a type of administration that contributes primarily to reconciling and synthesizing the work of a wide spectrum of highly competent specialists (as in research). Some need a type that primarily provides in-service training and professional tools (as in an Extension Bureau). Creative administration provides latitude within which each agency can develop a style of administration appropriate to its responsibility.

Moreover, each subordinate agency has a sufficiently unique task that it becomes important to give the head of each division and bureau wide operating autonomy. Only by giving such latitude to the head of each subordinate agency can the tendency to remove important activities from the ministry and give them to autonomous agencies outside the ministry be overcome.

This operating autonomy needs to include wide authority to incur expenditures within the established budget, with authority to transfer funds between line items. Only the head of an agency can really know what pattern of expenditures within established program purposes gives promise of being most productive. To have to go through lengthy chains of comment and decision to get approval of individual expenditures hampers many ministries of agriculture as well as national governments.

Administrative experimentation. Creative administration involves a constant search for more effective methods. Public agrisupport services provide fruitful opportunities for administrative experimentation. Far too often, an extension service or a credit program is set up on a uniform pattern throughout a country after perhaps lengthy debates as to just how it should be organized and conducted. How much better it would be, in many instances, where alternative ways of conducting the activity are available, to try several of them out, following one pattern in some districts, another pattern in other districts, and sometimes even a third and fourth pattern in others, and then compare results. To be open-minded with respect to administrative patterns is one of the marks of a creative administrator, but to be "experiment-minded" is even better.[17]

Encouraging upward communication. In far too many organizations, one could substitute the terms "speaker" and "listeners" for the terms "superior" and "subordinate" officers. Even when the boss would wish it otherwise, the pattern is for him to speak and for them to listen and comply. However, most organizations are more effective when the top officer encourages his subordinates to express their views and make suggestions without fear of penalty and with assurance that they will receive due credit for their contributions. The administrator who inhibits his subordinates from giving him their views robs his organization of their potential contributions and deadens the enthusiasm of his staff.

Encouraging lateral consultation. Another feature of creative administration is its encouragement of lateral consultation between subordinate officers of different divisions of organization. Yet freedom for lateral consultation is not widespread. It is inhibited both by rigid concepts of "orderly" line administration and by the unwillingness of many administrators to trust their subordinates. Obviously, final decisions must be made according to an established pattern, but lateral consultation in the formula-

---

[17] See A. T. Mosher, "Administrative Experimentation as a Way of Life for Developmental Projects," *International Development Review,* Vol. IX, No. 2 (June 1967), pp. 38-41.

tion of proposals can usually expedite final decision-making by discovering areas of agreement and precise points of disagreement. It also can greatly reduce the pressure on the time and energies of decision-making administrators.

Continuous staff development. Finally, creative administration includes a determined and continuing effort at staff development. In many countries this will require revised practices with respect to promotions so that men entering the service at subordinate levels have the opportunity through proved competence to keep advancing to more and more responsible positions. It requires adequate salaries. It requires regular and persistent programs of in-service training within each division. Above all, it requires a special attitude toward their colleagues and subordinates by administrators and supervisors at all levels—an attitude of interest in the professional growth of each person on the staff for his own sake, not just as a cog in the bureaucratic machine.

Unless creative administration is achieved in carrying out the program of a ministry, no form of organization, however appropriate, can be highly effective.

Chapter 5

A SUGGESTED FORM OF ORGANIZATION

To venture beyond the general considerations and principles discussed in the preceding chapter is a dangerous undertaking. It is one thing to list requirements, but to propose a specific form of organization that might honor those requirements is to invite controversy. Yet that is precisely what needs to be done, country-by-country, if the organization of ministries of agriculture is to be made more effective. Variations among countries may be justified by differing local conditions, of which the size of a country and its general form of government are only two. Nevertheless, at least as a basis for discussion, this chapter outlines a suggested structure for a ministry of agriculture, during that period when a country is intent on creating a modern agriculture.

I would begin by making two decisions. The first decision would be to include within the ministry of agriculture all public activities that bear primarily on agricultural production, growth and adjustment, leaving to other ministries all activities that, although they may affect agriculture, are more closely related to the central responsibilities of other ministries. This decision would involve, in most countries, bringing within the ministry of agriculture several independent agricultural agencies.

The second decision would be to handle the problem of balancing autonomy and coordination by giving substantial operating autonomy to each major division of the ministry while simultaneously setting up specific arrangements for coordination among them. This would return a large measure of autonomy to previously independent agencies, and would extend similar autonomy to other major divisions of the ministry, most of which need it just as much.

MAJOR DIVISIONS CORRESPONDING TO COMPONENTS OF AGRICULTURAL GROWTH

Having made those two decisions, my next step would be to suggest that the ministry should contain six major divisions,[18] corresponding to the six elements of public activity for agricultural growth identified in Chapter 4:

1. Research
2. Provision of Production Inputs
3. Rural Agri-Support Infrastructure
4. Farmers' Incentives and Agricultural Prices
5. Land Development and Management
6. Agricultural Manpower Training

The *Division of Research* would be responsible for conducting research on major crops and livestock, soils, farm management, engineering related to farm production and marketing, the technology and economics of marketing agricultural products, the demand for farm products, and, in appropriate cases, research on new uses for farm products. Part of its research would be conducted at a national research station, part of it within each agricultural region having either immediate or future growth poten-

[18] Nomenclature varies with respect to levels of organization in different countries. In this discussion a "Division" is the top level of organization within a ministry. Each Division, in turn, would normally be composed of several "Bureaus." An "Office" is the name given to a unit that affects, works through, or requires the cooperation of bureaus in more than one major "Division."

tial, and part of it as a component in the program of faculties of agriculture, supported by grants from the ministry.

While most of the personnel of the Division of Research would be directly engaged in research, with many of them doing some teaching, some might be "subject-matter specialists" to serve as direct liaison personnel between research and extension. Subject-matter specialists would then work in close cooperation with the Bureau of Extension or with regional extension supervisors, advising local extension workers and participating in their in-service training.

The Division of Research would concentrate its attention on problems of both the IGP and the FGP Areas of the country. With respect to IGP Areas it should keep searching for technologies that can further increase production of each region's major farm products, that can decrease costs of production, that can cope with pests and diseases. With respect to areas of future growth potential it has the important task of developing new technologies that can bring more and more FGP Areas into the IGP category.

The *Division of Production Inputs* would have the responsibility for taking such public action as might be needed to insure an adequate (wholesale) supply of fertilizers, seeds, pesticides and farm equipment to allow each agricultural region of the nation to utilize its current agricultural potential to the full and to capitalize quickly on new opportunities for growth as they arise. To discharge that responsibility the division would keep a running record of current inventories of these commodities; it would keep abreast of current consumption of each, region by region; it would project probable demand for each over the next two to three years. Based on this information, the division would take steps to assure that the supply of these inputs keeps pace with demand. In some cases, the needed action would be to assure adequate imports, whether through private or public channels. In other cases it would be to stimulate, facilitate, and sometimes make direct arrangements for domestic manufacture (or, in the case of seeds, multiplication).

57

How wide and/or intricate the activities of this division need to be will vary from country to country and from time to time depending on how much reliance is placed on the private sector and how much on direct public management. However, a separate division of the ministry is needed to concentrate on providing production inputs in adequate amounts in either case. To the extent that provision of inputs is privately managed, certain types of regulation (such as seed certification) are needed and, if imports are required, estimates of needs must be prepared for inclusion in overall planning. To the extent that production of selected farm inputs is publicly managed, the ministry of agriculture, even if not itself responsible for managing production, needs to take the same steps as though the management were in private hands, to assure that supply keeps up with demand.

The *Division of Rural Agri-Support Infrastructure* (which, for the sake of simplicity, might be called the Division for Rural Services) would be responsible for creating and operating a "Progressive Rural Structure."

Precisely what activities need to be carried on by this Division depends on a number of factors. The choice depends, first, on how many of its elements are provided as governmental services. Agricultural extension almost always is. Local verification trials should be. The construction and maintenance of roads is almost always a public activity, but it is likely to be entrusted to a different ministry. The distribution of farm inputs, the marketing of farm products, and the provision of production credit can be provided by private merchants and bankers, or through cooperative societies, or by governmental agencies, or by two or all of these.

It is not my recommendation that all elements of a Progressive Rural Structure be public activities, or that the construction and maintenance of rural roads be a responsibility of the Ministry of Agriculture. Still, the fact that concern about the complete rural agri-support infrastructure has not been focused in a single agency in the past has undoubtedly contributed to its neglect and to the prevalence of uneven and unwise investment in different ele-

Major Divisions of a Ministry of Agriculture

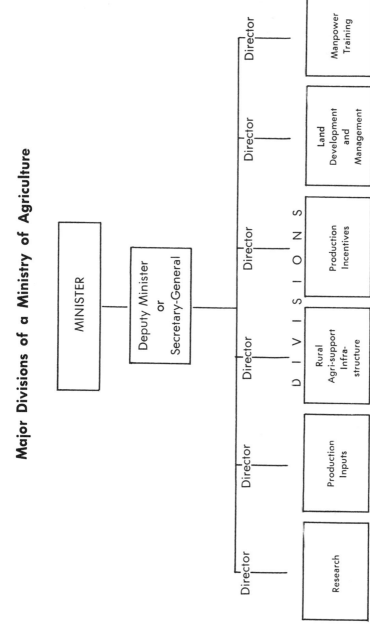

(This is a partial outline showing major divisions only. The suggested organization of a Ministry of Agriculture is shown in greater detail in the chart on page 67.)

ments of it. Regardless of what agencies, public or private, are responsible for providing different elements of a Progressive Rural Structure, each element depends on all the others for its effectiveness. It takes *all* of these agri-support services to make each *farming locality* highly effective. Any one of them alone—extension, or credit, or markets, or verification trials, or outlets for farm supplies and equipment—is of limited value in the absence of the others. Consequently, whatever responsibility the Ministry of Agriculture may have with respect to various ones of them should be delegated to a single division of the ministry.

Even where elements of a Progressive Rural Structure lie in the private sector, or are administratively related to other ministries, it is the Ministry of Agriculture that should have ultimate responsibility for seeing to it that all agricultural regions of the country are adequately served by a complete Progressive Rural Structure as rapidly as they are ready to utilize it. That means providing a complete PRS in all IGP Areas as rapidly as possible and a skeleton[19] PRS in all FGP Areas.

Each element of a Progressive Rural Structure can be administered by a separate bureau but all should be grouped together in a single Division to insure their integration.

The *Division of Production Incentives* would have as its primary tasks, first, to keep abreast of what is happening to farmers' incentives, region by region; second, to analyze the probable impact of alternative changes that might be made; and, third, to recommend changes that could improve the situation. This does *not* mean that every government should adopt price control policies and/or establish subsidies affecting agriculture. Nor can a ministry of agriculture control the many governmental tax, monetary and price policies that have effects far beyond agriculture, or shift land tenure policies at will. But every Ministry of Agriculture does need a division that can keep the minister informed as to what the present situation is, that can propose policy modifications and public programs that would help, and

---

[19] See explanation in footnote on page 24.

that can administer related programs that may be undertaken. By having a concern about farmers' incentives overall, instead of just for prices, or for tax or land tenure policies only, it can view the problem as a whole, taking into account the interrelationships among all of the factors bearing on farmers' production incentives.[20]

In considering what policies to recommend, the Division of Farmers' Incentives should consider their impact on the non-farm economy as well as on agricultural production. It must be interested in the strength of farmers' incentives, to be sure, but when prices of farm products are raised to favor farmers they may work against the interests of urban consumers. If the Ministry of Agriculture's division for this topic does not take the interests of urban consumers into account in its recommendations, the fight over such prices in the planning commission or in parliament will be an adversary confrontation rather than a discussion based on recommendations that already have taken both rural and urban interests into account. Consequently, the division needs to have economists on its staff who are as competent in fiscal, monetary, tax and price policy as in the special concerns of agriculture.

The *Division of Land Development and Management* would be responsible for ministry activities related to irrigation, drainage, land clearing and leveling, field consolidation, soil conservation, and the management of public lands. How extensive these activities may be will vary greatly from country to country. In some cases, major (and sometimes even minor) irrigation works are the responsibility of a separate ministry. Where they are, it is still important for the agriculture ministry's Division of Land Development and Management to pay attention both to proposals for new public projects of all sizes and to opportunities for on-the-farm land development, since choices frequently have to be made among them because of limited resources. Moreover,

---

[20] For a discussion of these interrelationships, see *The World Food Problem, op. cit.,* Vol. II, pp. 504-35.

the very widespread criticism of the design of irrigation projects as paying most attention to engineering features and very little to requirements for maximum agronomic effectiveness underscores the need for the Ministry of Agriculture at least to have an organized capacity to assure adequate attention to agronomic considerations of all land development projects, by whomever administered. Similarly, assuring adequate attention to drainage, both in irrigation projects and elsewhere, requires an organized capacity to deal with it.

Every country has some publicly owned land that is used at least partially for agricultural purposes. Who is to manage such land? The argument for assigning the task to a Division of Land Development and Management is to facilitate coordination of policy with respect to the use of all public lands. Grazing, logging, the use of public lands as catchment basins for water and for water storage, the clearing of forested areas for agricultural settlement: all of these are interacting, they are both complementary and competitive. Consequently, land management and land development need to be entrusted to different bureaus but within a single division of the Ministry of Agriculture.

Whether the management of state farming enterprises, where they exist, should be the responsibility of this division is a difficult question, too difficult to examine here. There are strong arguments for setting up at least the larger of such enterprises under a separate administrative agency. There are equally strong arguments for merging their management with the management of other public lands. Where the problem becomes particularly difficult is where major export crops are grown mostly by large estates under public management, while other crops are grown privately on small farms. If management of state farms is separated from the ministry of agriculture in such cases, the result is to divide administrative units along commodity lines and set up different power structures for (big) state farms and (small) private farms. That is not good. If, on the other hand, the decision is to entrust the management of state farms to the Division of Land Development within the Ministry of Agriculture, that division may assume an unwieldly size. Whichever way the decision goes, it is important to bring the needs for growth in state-managed farms into the planning process in such a way that the needs for growth of both state and privately operated farming operations receive appropriate attention.

The *Division of Manpower Training* would address itself to the problem of increasing the number, and improving the occupational quality, of those who engage professionally in one or another agri-support activity, whether public or private.

Consequently, the task of the Division of Manpower Training is partly to be concerned about the programs of agricultural schools and colleges, whether or not they are administered by the Ministry of Agriculture. It is partly to keep surveying the adequacy of the number of trained personnel of various needed types that are forthcoming and make recommendations about additional training facilities that may be required. It is partly to keep abreast of the in-service training programs of all agencies in the ministry and determine what additional training opportunities may be needed. It is partly to serve as a producer of, and as a clearing house for, training materials that can be used in all types of in-service training related to agri-support activities.

This division might, but in my judgment should not, have responsibility for administering the extension service. Instead, the extension service should be the responsibility of a bureau within the Division of Rural Infrastructure, for two reasons.

First, the mutual complementarities among all of the elements of a Progressive Rural Structure—local markets for farm inputs and products, farm credit, local verification trials, extension services and rural transport—are so strong that I believe that public activities with respect to them should all be in the same division.

Second, I believe that the mandate of the extension service should be broader than it is usually conceived. Certainly the task of helping individual farmers make the best use of the production opportunities available to them is central to its mandate. But wherever extension services have been conspicuously successful, I think we will find that they have taken initiative in *expanding* those opportunities by finding ways to get other elements of a Progressive Rural Structure introduced or improved in specific farming localities. The same procedure it follows in helping farmers adjust to more modern farming can with equal value be used to help private merchants and lenders make similar adjustments in line with the new needs of a modern agriculture.[21] Full use of these opportunities, it seems to me, would be easier to achieve by housing the Bureau of Extension alongside those serving other elements of a Progressive Rural Structure in the Division of Rural Infrastructure.

To summarize, then, it seems to me that a ministry of agriculture, in circumstances where creating a modern agriculture is a paramount concern, might well be organized into six major divisions:

1. A Division of Research
2. A Division of Production Inputs
3. A Division of Rural Agri-Support Infrastructure
4. A Division of Production Incentives and Agricultural Prices
5. A Division of Land Development and Management
6. A Division of Manpower Training

THREE "OFFICES"

In addition to six major divisions, a ministry of agriculture needs to have three "offices" to accomplish three types of co-operation and coordination among the six major divisions:

1. An Office of Statistical Services
2. An Office of Integrated Projects
3. An Office of Planning

Office of statistical services. Under all circumstances, the collection and collation of agricultural statistics is considered an im-

---

[21] For a discussion of the various role of extension workers, see *The World Food Problem, op. cit.,* Vol. II, pp. 532-35.

portant activity of national governments, sometimes handled by a Ministry of Agriculture, sometimes by a central statistical office for the whole government, frequently by two or four or ten or twelve governmental agencies without consultation or cooperation.

There is not likely to be much quarrel with the proposition that all or most of the collection and collation of agricultural statistics undertaken within a Ministry of Agriculture should be centralized in one office. Where there is likely to be debate is over questions of what statistics are to be collected and how. One gains the impression, substantiated by World Bank experience, that many of the types of data needed in planning are not now being collected in most countries. A single office directed to integrate the data needs of each division organized along the lines I have suggested might help to remedy this shortcoming.

Office of integrated projects. The second coordinating office needed in each Ministry of Agriculture is an Office of Integrated Projects.

At issue here is the question of what organizational arrangements are to be made for special crop or livestock campaigns to accelerate the adoption of available new technologies. The advisability of having such campaigns is not at issue, but there is a strong tendency to set each such project up with its own complete field staff under independent administration rather than to utilize the staff and facilities of existing units of a ministry. Put another way, there is a strong tendency to compensate for inadequate *regular* rural agri-support infrastructure by creating a special one, *ad hoc,* for each special project undertaken, or, alternatively, to give the agri-support infrastructure inadequate attention, assuming that all that is needed is an intensified extension program.

There are two basic objections to this customary procedure. One is that it is wasteful in that it leads to great duplication of staff and, in the process, moves the most promising technological opportunities away from the responsibility of the "regular" governmental services. The other is that it delays giving explicit attention to a complete rural agri-support infrastructure to serve the totality of a modern agriculture.

What the *ad hoc* project approach can accomplish, on the other hand, is an effective coordination of many different activities that bear on the adoption by farmers of the particular technology being pushed; it can bring the distribution of production inputs, the provision of credit, extension teaching, and marketing into effective interaction.

One way to achieve the advantages of special crop or livestock projects without setting up a separate staff and facilities for each of them is to establish an Office of Integrated Projects in the Ministry of Agriculture. Each project would have a coordinator whose task would be to work out a plan of operations with the head of each bureau of the ministry that should be involved, and to keep track of, and report on progress being made to the minister.

Another type of project susceptible to this approach is land settlement and/or irrigation schemes that depend for their success on a rapid expansion of agri-support services and perhaps on some new research as well. Still another is integrated projects directed specifically at the problems of small farms.

In other words, an Office of Integrated Projects would be a device *within* a ministry to achieve the results of a coordinated attack on each particular problem and the exploitation of each particular opportunity. It would reduce duplication of effort and increase coordination. *And it would focus the efforts of the regular bureaus of the ministry on a succession of high priority activities.*

Office of planning. The third special coordinating office in an effective Ministry of Agriculture should be its Office of Planning. This office is of crucial importance if the ministry is to be a major force in planning to create a modern agriculture. It is here that the base can be laid for integrating planning, budgeting and implementation.

Expanded Outline of Suggested Organization
MINISTRY OF AGRICULTURE

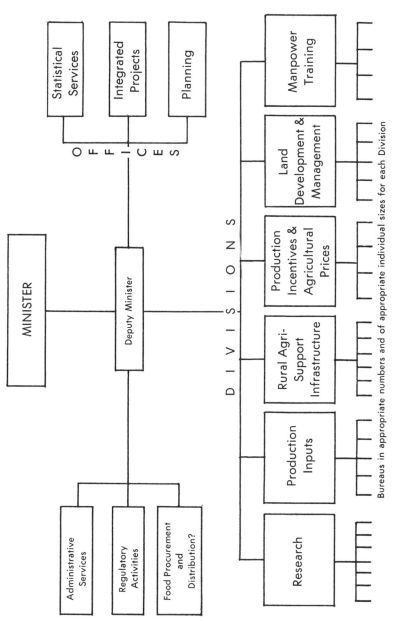

Bureaus in appropriate numbers and of appropriate individual sizes for each Division

Actual planning should not be done solely by a separate full-time staff of this office. Instead, while there should be a relatively small full-time staff of the office, its members should be joined in formulating and revising each plan by representatives of three other groups:

1. the six major divisions of the ministry and the other two coordinating offices;
2. representatives of field agricultural development officers serving in the major agricultural regions of the country;[22]
3. representatives of the other ministries having responsibilities related to agriculture.

Each of these groups of representatives has a unique role to play in the planning process.[23]

Those who are full-time members of the staff of the Office of Planning should bring to its deliberations an overall perspective on the task, unbiased by personal involvement in any of the operating divisions of the ministry or in the problems of any specific agricultural region of the country. They also have a special liaison role between agricultural planning and overall economic planning.

The role of the representatives of each of the major divisions and of the other two offices of the ministry is both to initiate budget requests with respect to the on-going activities of each and to formulate specific project proposals with respect to new activities that are under consideration. Their proposals thus include both so-called "development" and "non-development" as-

---

[22] See Appendix B on page 142.

[23] "Development planning puts a special premium on cooperation within government. Ideally, a plan should be prepared with the cooperation and participation of every interested party, both within and outside government. However, a comprehensive or partial development plan can be, and often is, formulated by a few technicians, sometimes assisted by foreign experts, without much recourse to governmental administrative machinery. But it is impossible to implement a plan in this way. A government must usually rely heavily on its administrative apparatus to prepare and carry out projects and programs. . . . It is at this point that the condition of a country's public administration is usually seen to limit development policy and planning." Albert Waterston, *Development Planning: Lessons of Experience* (Baltimore: Johns Hopkins University Press, 1965), p. 251.

OFFICE OF PLANNING
MINISTRY OF AGRICULTURE

Minister of Agriculture
Chief of Office of Planning
Full-time Staff

_____

_____

_____

_____

_____

_____

Representatives of Agricultural Regions

_____

_____

_____

_____

_____

Representatives of Divisions and Offices of the Ministry of Agriculture

_____   _____

_____   _____

_____   _____

_____   _____

Representatives of Other Ministries Having Related Responsibilities

_____

_____

_____

_____

pects of their respective activities. They include what each division does that is really part of agricultural production, that which contributes to agricultural growth, and that which helps achieve desirable adjustment both within agriculture and between agriculture and other parts of the economy.

The role of representatives of agricultural development officers from different major agricultural regions is, first, to present to the Office of Planning the judgment of agricultural development officers of each region as to desirable changes or new emphases to be introduced into their regions in the near future and, second, to participate in the discussion as to where different elements of the total program should be emphasized in the immediate future.

The role of the Office of Integrated Projects in the planning process is to help work out the respective responsibilities of different divisions in whatever integrated projects are to be continued or launched in the next year. Not all integrated projects will involve more than one division but most are likely to if duplication or overlapping responsibilities are to be avoided. Since the Office of Integrated Projects will be involved in monitoring the implementation of projects that involve activities by more than one division, it should be a party to planning them as well. The budgets for projects involving two or more divisions should be in the budgets for those divisions, but the plan of work (of each division) on which the budgets are based should go to the Office of Integrated Projects for its guidance in monitoring and reporting on implementation.

The role of representatives of other ministries having responsibilities related to agriculture is to serve as an informational and consultative link in both directions. They can inform agriculture's Office of Planning about relevant programs and plans in other ministries. They can inform their own ministries about what is being considered in the Ministry of Agriculture. And they can help work out mutual adjustments in plans where these are required.

We shall go into the procedures of this Office of Planning more fully in Chapter 8.

Divisions of unequal size. One argument that can be urged against this proposed form of organization is that it would result in divisions of unequal size, both in number of personnel and in size of budgets. It certainly would do that. There would undoubtedly be a tendency for the heads of the larger divisions to wield the most influence, and a tendency for the heads of smaller divisions to try to expand their empires.

But the point of the form proposed is that where agricultural growth is the chief goal, the form of organization should be built around that need and facilitate an effective linking of planning, budgeting and implementation. In my judgment it is more important for the heads of major divisions to represent the main components of agricultural growth than it is to try to achieve divisions of more equal physical and fiscal size, a situation that is seldom achieved in practice in any case.

Confusing staff and line functions. Another possible objection is that this system blurs the usual distinction between line and staff functions, since each division would administer certain programs but would gather information and make recommendations to the minister with respect to others. Again, it seems to me it is better to keep divisions organized by major components of agricultural growth, even at the cost of introducing some staff-line ambiguity, and then to take steps to resolve that problem by appropriate organization *within* each division.

Abandoning the conventional agriculture-livestock-forestry-fisheries form of organization. One knowledgeable critic has insisted that the conventional organization of a ministry into this four-fold division must be retained, no matter what other innovations may be introduced. I disagree with this criticism with respect to separating agriculture and livestock as major divisions of a ministry, or as separate ministries. The complementarities between crop and livestock production are so strong that they should be the responsibility of a single ministry and of the same

71

divisions of that ministry. As for forestry and fisheries, it is completely beyond my competence even to comment on them. I simply do not know where their interests should be represented within a governmental structure, but I do not believe that they should comprise separate major agencies within a ministry of agriculture just because they have in the past.

No bureau of agricultural economics? A fourth major criticism has been that my plan of organization does not include a separate and prominent "Bureau of Agricultural Economics." One critic said, "the Bureau of Agricultural Economics is the Number One staff agency of a modern ministry of agriculture."

Having been trained as an agricultural economist myself I have considered that criticism seriously, but have not changed my proposal because of it. I assume that several full-time members of the Office of Planning would be agricultural economists. Their skills are essential to the planning process but should not be allowed to dominate it. Technological, geographical, and administrative considerations are important also, and economists may neglect them. I assume further that there probably would be a Bureau of Agricultural Economics within the Division of Research, and that members of that staff would devote part of their attention to policy-oriented research, as well as participating in the design and analysis of agronomic and livestock experimentation so that economic aspects of those studies are taken into account. Moreover, the Division of Farmers' Incentives would have agricultural and general economists on its staff, as should the Division of Land Development and the Division of Production Inputs. For the same reasons that I resist having special units parallel to other academic disciplines (except perhaps in the Division of Research), I resist it for agricultural economics in favor of organization by major problem areas. It might be a good idea to have a regular but informal series of consultations and seminars involving all social scientists in the ministry, but I believe it would be better not to have all of them segregated in a single bureau.

THE RATIONALE RESTATED

The form of organization for a ministry of agriculture recommended in this chapter is based on no colonial pattern and on the current pattern of no western or so-called "advanced" economy. Instead, it is a form of organization designed especially for countries for which creating a modern agriculture is currently of great importance: countries now moving into increasingly commercial farming, countries that have at their disposal improved technologies pertinent in some but not all of their agricultural regions, countries in which much can still be done through land improvement to increase the productivity of their agricultural resources, countries that need to improve their facilities for dealing with a much bigger volume of farm products than has moved through commercial channels in the past.

The best form of organization may be quite different later on after the structure for a modern agriculture has been fully achieved.

Second, the form of organization proposed here is an attempt to suggest a form of organization that will allow a close integration of planning, budgeting, and implementation. It does that partly by proposing a set of operating divisions that is parallel to what I believe should be the major elements of agricultural planning. And it does it partly by proposing a pattern of planning that allows those who will be responsible for implementation to have an active voice in planning.

Third, it is an attempt to outline a form of organization that will allow specific programs to have as much independence as they need and that will accomplish that purpose without taking them out of the ministry of agriculture. It does that by giving each division a large measure of independence within the ministry while coordinating their activities through the Office of Planning and the Office of Integrated Projects. At the same time, it allows all activities that are directly and primarily related to agriculture to be organized in a way that allows planning for agriculture to be initiated within the ministry of agriculture; it overcomes the problem of having to leave overall agricultural planning to the Planning Commission, as must be done when many important agricultural programs are conducted by independent agencies outside the ministry.

Fourth, it proposes a set of divisions each of which is problem-oriented in a manner consistent with the unique characteristics of agriculture as an industry that were discussed in Chapter 1, and parallel to the chief tasks in creating a modern agriculture. A ministry is not a university. Its tasks do not parallel academic disciplinary lines. Bureaus of plant industry, animal industry, agricultural economics, agricultural engineering, etc., may be appropriate within the Division of Research of a ministry, provided the organization of that division also makes provision for interdisciplinary attacks on specific problems. But they are not an appropriate basis for organizing an entire ministry into major divisions. Instead, I contend that each major division of a ministry should deal with an important specific type of problem, particularly from the standpoint of achieving agricultural growth, and be staffed by persons representing all types of specialized knowledge that are pertinent to that problem.

Fifth, it groups the major activities of the ministry into only six major divisions, resulting in a manageable span of control for the minister and for the deputy minister or secretary-general in charge of those six major divisions. With this form of organization, when the minister sits down with his chief lieutenants—the directors of divisions—there would be gathered about the table representatives of the six major components of agricultural growth and of achieving a modern agriculture.

Better models than the one I have proposed may be possible, and we should try to develop them. But I would contend that whatever model is utilized by a country in South or Southeast Asia in the decade of the 1970s should be subjected to these five tests.

Part III

PLANNING TO CREATE
A MODERN AGRICULTURE

The general nature of the problem of achieving agricultural growth is implied by the characteristics of agriculture discussed in Chapter 1, and by the section on "promoting agricultural growth" in Chapter 2.

Farming is a biological production process that is not commodity-specific. Most of its production inputs can be applied to the production of any of a wide variety of crops—the same sunlight, irrigation water, fertilizers, human labor, non-human draft power, and even some pesticides can be used to produce wheat, cotton, sugarcane, tobacco or betel nuts. What combination of commodities a farmer chooses to produce is determined by the local climate, relative local prices of both products and inputs, his knowledge and skill with respect to alternatives, the availability of agri-support services and family needs for consumption. Planning for agricultural growth, therefore, can more effectively be applied to improving the public and private agri-support services avail-

75

able to farmers, in each of their widely dispersed farming locali-
ties, and to improving the agri-milieu (including, particularly,
more favorable price and tenure relationships) than to overt
efforts to secure a planned increase in one or more specific com-
modities.

In the process of trying to accelerate agricultural growth, pub-
lic policy and planning should take account of the fact that indi-
vidual farms range all the way from largely subsistence to largely
commercial operations. It should recognize that different parts of
the country have vastly differing potentials for agricultural growth
and adopt programs especially tailored to fit the needs of each.
And it should take due cognizance of the fact that agriculture as
a whole is always partly a private and partly a public activity
that needs simultaneously to serve both private and public ob-
jectives.

Chapter 6

GENERAL COMMENTS ON
AGRICULTURAL PLANNING

OBJECTIVES

A government almost always has more than one objective in whatever planning it may do with respect to agriculture. The one most frequently emphasized is growth of agricultural production in either physical or market value terms. But even where that objective is emphasized, others are almost always being taken into account either explicitly or implicitly. The allocation of public revenues to accelerate agricultural growth may be less than it otherwise would be because of foreign exchange considerations or because of judgments with respect to the estimated rate of return on investments in different sectors of the national economy. Increasingly, also, the impact of specific measures designed to accelerate agricultural growth on employment opportunities and on income distribution are also being taken into account.

To create a modern agriculture. The thesis being presented throughout this book is that the time has come in countries of South and Southeast Asia when, for at least the next fifteen to twenty-five years, primacy should be given to the objective of creating the facilities and services of a truly modern agriculture. This can be done economically in some regions of each country much more rapidly than in others. In some regions of each it cannot be done at all within the foreseeable future. But the argument presented here is that, for the next decade or two, the goal of creating a modern agriculture should be primary.

In general, major attention is now being given to getting the most growth possible out of existing technology and in the areas where it can be applied. Inadequate attention is being given to searching for additional new technology, with respect to more crops and livestock, and to expanding the areas served by all of the features of a modern agriculture, so that both present and new technology yet to come can spread rapidly within them. The situation on this point is mixed, because some investments are being made in major irrigation projects, and some attention is being given to searching for additional new technologies, but not enough.

To argue that the goal of creating a modern agriculture should be given primacy for the next decade or two is *not* to suggest that no concurrent attention should be given to other objectives. It was pointed out in Chapter 2 that there are two ways to increase agricultural production. One is to take measures to increase the degree to which present opportunities for greater production are actually exploited; the other is to expand the capacity of the agricultural industry for future production. An emphasis on creating a modern agriculture stresses the expansion of the *capacity* of the agricultural industry. Simultaneously, however, efforts should continue to be made to get the most production possible out of current capacity.

Consequently, while giving primary emphasis to creating a modern agriculture, other objectives of agricultural planning continue to be important.

To increase the value added in agriculture. Even with respect to food production—and agriculture can and does produce much more than that—a productive agriculture is desirable not so much because it produces food as because it can produce *income* for individual farmers and for the nation. Families and nations can have enough to eat if they have sufficient income, no matter how that income is earned. Food can be purchased, and it can be imported if it is not produced in sufficient quantities and variety domestically.

Consequently, the basic reason why agricultural growth is so important in many countries is not because people need more food. Instead, it is because so many and such a high percentage of the people are dependent on farming for their income and because alternative employment opportunities are so limited.

It is because of the predominant importance of this income aspect of agriculture that it is better to plan and conduct public agricultural activities so as to surround farmers by more profitable opportunities to engage in the biological processes of farming, regardless of what they produce, than it is to plan primarily to increase the production of specific farm commodities. Each farmer is more likely to squeeze more income out of the resources of his own farm and location if he is free to select his own pattern of production than if he is forced to grow certain crops in order to help meet commodity targets.

To provide remunerative employment. The current high rates of population increase in nearly every country involve, inevitably, a rapid rise in the size of the labor force and in the number of dependent families. So long as family income is dependent on productive employment, it is only those families that have at least one working member who can share in what the country produces or imports. Moreover, the capital cost of increasing non-farm employment is sufficiently high that there is no hope within at least the next generation of creating new non-farm jobs any faster—and probably not as fast—as the size of the labor force will increase. Consequently, agriculture will have to continue to provide employment for at least as many people in each country as it does now, and probably for many more, if increasing numbers of workers are not to remain unemployed.

The careful methods of cultivation that can wring the maximum production advantage out of the new high-yielding cereal varieties usually require additional labor per acre. Growing more than one crop in each field each year also increases labor requirements. Such multiple cropping requires that each crop be harvested and the next crop planted within as short a period as possible, and to accomplish that, the substitution of tractor power for animal power becomes attractive and is frequently desirable even though it results in a net decrease in labor requirements for harvesting and land preparation when considered alone.

In view of the need for more employment opportunities, the practice of many governments of subsidizing the increased use of tractors by preferential import duties is probably a mistake. Subsidies increase the profitability to individual farmers of shifting to tractors. They do this by substituting a public cost (equal to the subsidy) for a private cost. While doing that they impose the additional public cost of dealing with the increased employment problem that introduction of the tractors may create.

Thus, different aspects of increasing the value-added in agriculture have employment effects that may work in opposite directions. Sorting out their net effect, under different sets of local circumstances, becomes very difficult.[24] Yet impact on employment opportunities must be a major factor in agricultural planning.

Meanwhile, overall national economic planning must give major attention to increasing *non-farm* employment, even in the interest of increasing farm incomes, partly to provide more employment outside agriculture and partly to increase the domestic market for farm products.

---

[24] It is important to keep the focus on total agricultural employment opportunities, not just on farm labor requirements. Operating agri-support activities requires more and more workers as farming becomes more commercial. Shifting from animal to tractor power reduces farm employment partly by speeding up field operations and partly by ending the need for labor in caring for work animals. It simultaneously creates employment in servicing tractors and in distributing fuel. Tractorization affects the foreign exchange position also, if tractors and/or fuels have to be imported. Domestic production of tractors can provide some employment, but the capital cost per worker employed is rather high.

To reduce rural poverty. There was a time when the statement would go unchallenged that the task of a ministry of agriculture is to foster agricultural growth and that rural welfare will then improve automatically. Not so today! Countries whose agriculture is relatively advanced have learned that it is possible for much of their agriculture to become commercial and highly productive and still have large numbers of rural people who are very poor. Farmers who have larger farms have, in general, greater income opportunities, and as increases in production become possible the tendency is for farmers who have access to financial resources (usually the larger farmers) to increase the size of their farms even more. Farm operators, in general, have greater income possibilities than landless farm laborers. Farm owners usually have higher income possibilities than tenants. Farmers on better land usually have better income possibilities than those on poorer land.

"Poverty" has two meanings. It can mean "having very little" in an absolute sense, or it can be used to describe the plight of those who have much less than someone else, usually in the same society. When taken in the latter sense, poverty cannot be "eliminated"; there will always be a bottom 10% or 20% in any income distribution, even though the incomes of people in these lower brackets may be rising. What *can* be achieved is a reduced range of incomes so that the poorest 10% or 20% are not as far below the top 10% or 20% as they were before.

Reducing rural poverty is a possibility under either definition. The average level of rural incomes can rise in response to achieving greater "value-added" in agriculture if the number of people employed in it rises less rapidly. To achieve a more acceptable distribution of rural incomes is also possible but it requires other policies and forms of achievement. It is not achieved automatically by increasing agricultural production; instead, the effect of rising agricultural productivity is likely to make rural incomes less equalitarian than they were before unless other steps are taken to offset this tendency.

Rising rural incomes and an improved income distribution de-

81

pend on more than just increasing the value-added in agriculture in aggregate terms. They depend on the whole pattern of land tenure arrangements. They depend on the degree to which there is an active market for land. They depend on the presence or absence of alternative off-farm employment. They are affected by the form of various agri-support activities, both commercial or non-commercial: are these services equally available to all or only to the more affluent and powerful? They are influenced by the degree to which farmers themselves have an effective voice in their economic and political affairs.

OBJECTIVES OF AGRICULTURAL PLANNING

- *To create a modern agriculture.*
- To increase the value-added in agriculture.
- To provide remunerative employment.
- To reduce rural poverty.
- To overcome adverse foreign exchange situations.

Some aspects of rural welfare depend on factors quite separate from family incomes. They depend on the quality and form of non-agricultural rural public services such as education, health, police services and the courts, and on the mobility people have to stay where they are or to move elsewhere. They depend on the organization of community life and on the quality of inter-personal relationships: the sense of "belonging," the degree of felt affection, and on feelings of prestige or of personal value to the community.

Obviously many of these non-economic aspects of rural welfare lie outside the scope of agricultural planning, but the economic aspects do not. In every country there are pressures to reduce wide disparities of income, both between regions and between families in the same regions. Consequently, the reduction of rural poverty in both senses should be one of the objectives of agricultural planning.

To overcome adverse foreign exchange situations. An acceptable rate of modernization of agriculture and of modernization in general is not possible today without international trade. Certain types of machinery, certain chemicals and other essential production inputs almost always have to be imported, and these must be paid for by an equivalent value of exports.

What are the means by which agricultural planning can contribute effectively to solving the foreign exchange problem? Primarily by its allocation of research funds to selected types of research and by what it proposes with respect to farmers' incentives. Both of these can make it more profitable for farmers to produce commodities for which there is a foreign market or that can substitute for commodities now being imported.

Whether needed farm inputs are imported or produced domestically is also important. The importation of fertilizers, particularly, can absorb large quantities of foreign exchange. On the other hand, domestic fertilizer plants of economic size and type have a very high capital cost and employ very few workers. Consequently, the foreign exchange cost of importing fertilizers must be carefully weighed against the employment effect of investing large amounts of scarce capital in domestic production facilities.

All five of these objectives are important. The importance of each relative to each of the others will be different from place to place and from one time to another in the same place. In some cases there will be no conflict between them; the same measures can support two or more objectives. In other cases there will be a conflict, and giving more attention to one of them will necessitate being satisfied with less achievement toward one or another of the others.

CONTENTS OF AN AGRICULTURAL PLAN

Good agricultural planning involves much more than a proposed allocation of financial resources. That should be only the culmination. The prior tasks are to decide *what* ought to be done, *how, when, where* in the country and *by what agencies.* It is only on the basis of having answered these previous questions, and then having estimated the cost of each proposed activity, that the question of allocations can fruitfully be taken up. This may seem elementary, but development literature is full of references to plans that prescribe how much is to be spent in pursuit of specified targets but give no hint of the means to be employed, by whom, or where located within the country.[25]

A plan for agriculture should not be limited to capital investments nor just to projects to promote growth. It should cover, in addition, those activities by which public agencies participate in the agricultural production process: seed certification, the regulation of markets, plant protection research, market information services, etc. The reason for not trying to separate these from "development activities" in agricultural planning as stated earlier is primarily that both functions (plus, in some cases, programs of agricultural adjustment) must be carried on and both usually must be paid for out of the same public revenues. A secondary but important reason is that the three are not easily separated. Extension activities, for example, are part of current production insofar as they expand farmers' information about markets and technologies, but they are investment for future growth insofar as they increase the farm management abilities of the individual farmers.

An additional reason for including regular on-going public production activities in planning is to assure their periodical review. Everyone agrees that any governmental agency is much more easily established and expanded than it is contracted or abolished. Yet each such activity uses scarce resources, most of which are transferable with a little retraining or modification to other purposes. It is not economic to let established programs go on, year after year, consuming larger and larger budgets, without frequent

---

25 "Where plan formulation is viewed as an exclusive or isolated element divorced in practice if not in theory from plan implementation, as it has in fact been viewed in many countries, one finds that planners pay little attention in their plans to the choice of means to be employed to achieve plan targets. This is why most plans almost always provide detailed information only about *what* is to be achieved, but not about *how* to go about securing development objectives or targets or about *who* in government or elsewhere should be responsible for carrying out the required tasks." Waterston, *Development Planning, op. cit.*

review of what they are accomplishing, and at what cost. One must be skeptical of all available techniques for trying to quantify with precision the benefits of individual agri-support activities considered separately. The complementarities and joint products are too strong and too complex for that. But an annual review of each in connection with new budget requests as part of the planning process at least assures that there are frequent opportunities to consider the respective merits of maintaining or expanding current activities, or of curtailing one or more of them to free resources for other uses. It is reported that Nepal now has the practice of reviewing one of its important on-going activities each year, thus assuring that every such activity is thoroughly reviewed periodically, although not every year.

Any improvement in the effectiveness of public operations related to agriculture is equivalent to an investment since it contributes to greater production and growth in the future. It constitutes a change in the "quality of an input," just as does research that produces a more highly productive crop variety.

Consequently, the contents of a plan for agriculture should cover all public expenditures related to agricultural production, growth and adjustment: everything the ministry of agriculture is to do. This may present a problem in gearing it into a national development plan that may not follow the same procedures, but that problem can be handled by the ministry's Office of Planning by reclassifying proposed expenditures in a manner that will give the Planning Commission information it needs in the form in which it wants it.

THE PLANNING HORIZON: A "ROLLING" PLAN

A long-term plan for agriculture (ten to fifteen years) is needed for several reasons.

Some of the requirements for a modern agriculture require long construction periods. Establishing an adequate grid of farm-to-market roads is an example. Unless the size of the total task is estimated, and then divided into a number of annual stages consistent with getting the job completed within an acceptable period, the amount actually accomplished each year is likely to be grossly inadequate.

Activities that are launched in one year and completely in place within two or three may still have substantial maintenance or operating costs over a number of years into the future. These implications for future costs need to be shown in a long term plan before implementation is begun.

An important political reason for long-term planning is to allow the introduction of particular activities in different parts of the country to be phased over a period of years without having to bear the charge that some districts are being neglected. If the long-term plan clearly shows a particular activity to be started in some districts in year 1, is already scheduled to start in others in year 2, and in still others in year 3, etc., it is easier to justify the plan to legislators and the public. This phasing over time is particularly important in view of the need to tailor local programs to the immediacy of their potential for agricultural growth.

But while long-term planning is important it needs to be updated annually. Any long-term plan is bound to prove inadequate in practice unless revised annually, partly because costs change, partly because implementation may lag, partly because new technologies are almost certain to emerge. Consequently, the long-term plan needs to be revised annually, revising the plan for the ensuing year and adding a new tenth or fifteenth year at the end. It is the revised plan for the next ensuing year that becomes the ministry's budget proposal and the guide to immediate implementation.

Such a "rolling plan" is needed for good internal management of agricultural public activities whether the overall national development plan is formulated in that way or not. It is needed in district planning, in agency planning and in the final plan for agriculture by the Office of Planning. If agricultural planning is done in this manner, the ministry is always ready with pertinent proposals for consideration by the Planning Commission in formulating a new shorter-term plan or in revising it.

Chapter 7

PREPARATION OF ACTIVITY PROPOSALS

The basic raw material for an agricultural plan is a set of activity proposals. Whether these originate in connection with proposed plans for each farming district or as part of the proposals of agencies within the ministry each one needs to answer certain questions about the activity being proposed:

— What is intended to be accomplished by each program? (In quantitative terms, wherever that is quite predictable, but otherwise in words only. This estimate will be in terms of number of farmers reached, quantity of inputs distributed, etc., rather than an estimate of production increases.)

— By what plan of work are those objectives to be reached? (With a distribution of the "work load" and of the scheduled completion of instrumental objectives month by month or season by season through the year.)

— What are the estimated costs of the program by budget categories? (With those categories such that they can be analyzed in various ways, as explained by Waterston in *Development Planning: Lessons of Experience.*)[26]

— What are the priorities to be followed in case the requested allocation to the district or agency cannot be met in full? (The items to be dropped in case the final allocation is less than the amount requested may be whole projects, or they may be the same or differing percentages of several projects.)

— What provision is made for staff development? (Merit promotions, in-service training, etc.)

— Are proposed expansions of activities that have high complementarity with others matched by expansion of those other activities either in the same or in other agencies? (If they are not they will be of little value.)

— Does the agency have the administrative capacity to execute all parts of the program effectively?

To prepare activity proposals that can answer some of these questions satisfactorily, particularly those having to do with cost estimates and with what the activity is intended to accomplish, certain types of analysis and computation are useful.[27]

SPECIFYING ACTIVITY CHARACTERISTICS

The first step is to analyze each type of activity that must be performed in terms of each of three of its characteristics:

1. its simultaneous components,
2. its sequential components, and
3. the minimum effective unit for its expansion.

---

[26] "For a budget to be a reasonable efficient instrument for plan execution it must be a classification system which (a) permits allocations and expenditures to be related to specific projects, programs, and other purposes in a plan; (b) distinguishes between capital and current expenditures and receipts, and shows the extent of public savings (in the form of a surplus on current account) available for investment and (c) distinguishes between development and non-development expenditures on both capital and current account." Waterston, *Development Planning, op. cit.,* p. 218.

[27] These procedures are discussed at greater length, but in different terms, in *Creating a Progressive Rural Structure, op. cit.,* Appendix B, pp. 107-65.

Simultaneous components. Each activity has a number of simultaneous components for which budget provision must be made. For example, many tasks require simultaneous provision for salaries, physical facilities, and operating expenses. This is true of research programs, teaching programs, extension services, and regulatory activities. Many programs are less productive than they might be because one or another of these requirements is not adequately provided for. The most usual shortcoming is to put too much of the total amount into salaries and not enough into operating expenses such as teaching materials or funds for travel. Another frequent mistake is to allocate either too much or not enough for equipment.

Some activities require a fourth simultaneous component in addition: working capital. This is true of credit programs that require loan funds, and of marketing arrangements that must carry inventories of goods: whether of farm products or of farm inputs.

Moreover, some activities, however efficient they may be internally, are not very productive unless other activities are carried out in the same farming localities. It is this fact that leads to the advisability of having the bureaus of marketing, extension, credit, rural roads and local verification trials in the same Division of Rural Infrastructure and having any expansion of those activities carried out simultaneously in the same additional farming localities and districts each year. In other words, they are to be treated as a *single* activity having several simultaneous components. These simultaneous component characteristics of various tasks comprise some of the complementarities that must be a major criterion in allocative decision-making.

Sequential components. Another characteristic of each activity that should be analyzed in preparation for planning is the sequential components that make it up. For example, expanding a network of farm-to-market roads involves, first, deciding on the location of the new roads and making the necessary surveys;

second, obtaining the rights-of-way; third, constructing the roads; and fourth, making adequate arrangements for maintaining them. Or, in the case of an extension service it is necessary, first, to arrange facilities for training extension workers; second, to train the first group of workers; third, to launch the program to be carried on by those workers; and, fourth, to make adequate provision for continuing supervision and repeated in-service training. These steps cannot be taken simultaneously, they must be carried out sequentially with adequate time allotments for each step to be completed.[28]

Launching or expanding a research program, establishing a credit program, or starting or expanding an agricultural college, and most other essential tasks have similar sequential requirements.

Analyzing the sequential components of each activity is the basis for calculating some of the sequences and gestation periods that are major criteria in allocative decision-making. It is essential to phasing expenditures on individual activities over a period of years to fit within available resources.

Minimum effective units for expansion. The third characteristic of each activity that should be defined is the minimum size of an effective unit for its expansion.

In the process of making allocative decisions it is necessary constantly to choose between an increment of this and an increment of that. But how much is "an increment" in each case? Clearly one cannot add ½ of a truck or ⅓ of a pump. It may be possible to add three extension workers at the expense of one kilometer of rural road not built, but do three extension workers constitute an efficient increment? We need to determine the minimum *effective* unit for expansion of each activity and then

---

[28] Various publications that discuss so-called PERT analysis (Program Evaluation and Review Technique) can be helpful in accomplishing this phasing over time. The method is explained in simple terms in, U.S. Office of Economic Opportunity, *PERT for CAA Planning: A Programmed Course of Instruction in PERT,* OEO Training Manual 6321-1 (2 vols; Washington, D.C.: Executive Office of the President, 1969).

do our allocative planning in terms of incremental units of that size.

For example, an optimum unit for expanding an extension service is probably one that requires between twenty-five and thirty field extension workers working within a reasonable distance from each other, because that is the optimum size group for repeated in-service training and supervision. In the case of arranging adequate local retail outlets for farm inputs, the *farming district* is the minimum efficient unit of expansion because locality outlets must have direct ties to adequate wholesaling facilities and it is too expensive to provide these for less than one district. The minimum effective unit for research should probably be defined as that which provides all of the related scientific disciplines that are closely related to the particular commodity-oriented project or projects on which that unit of research is to work in the beginning. The minimum efficient size for a fertilizer factory is determined by the technology and economics of production, and by the demand for its product in its market area. The size of a gravity irrigation project may be determined by the amount of water available at a particular source, but if it is tube-well irrigation the unit of expansion can be determined by farm size, or by the size of available pumps, or by the demand for pumping power that will justify the cost of installing high-lines and transformers if electric power is to be used.

Thus each activity has its own appropriate criteria for establishing the minimum effective size for units of expansion. Establishing that effective size is important in order not to waste resources by spreading them over individual units that are too small in any one place to be effective and because it indicates the units in terms of which a large task should be phased over time.

Quantitative Requirements and Cost per Unit of Expansion

After the minimum unit of expansion for each activity is established, we can move to determining the quantitative requirements and estimating the cost per unit of expansion of each program activity. That can be done by taking into account both the simultaneous and the sequential components of each program at each stage of its development, estimating the number of personnel of different types and the physical equipment that will be needed, and translating this into a cost budget for salaries, for physical facilities, for operating expenses, and in some cases for operating capital also.

For later convenience in the planning process these costs per unit of expansion should list separately:

1. the requirements for personnel, in terms of numbers of persons with different types of training;
2. foreign exchange requirements; and
3. public expenditure requirements.

LAND AREA SERVED BY ONE UNIT OF EXPANSION

For some program activities, it is important to estimate the land area to be served by each unit of expansion. This is particularly true for rural agri-support infrastructure activities, because they should be treated as comprising a single activity later in the planning process and the minimum unit of expansion of each element of the program can serve different land areas, yet all must be coordinated to expand the infrastructure locality-by-locality and district-by-district.

Moreover, if the goal is set of creating a modern agriculture throughout current areas of immediate growth potential within a given number of years, the land area covered by each unit of expansion is needed in order to calculate how much has to be done each year if the goal is to be reached on time.

The unit of expansion for an extension service was defined as that to be served by twenty-five to thirty field workers. But this must be related to the land area to be served by each such unit, since an extension service should be expanded only in conjunction with other features of a rural agri-support infrastructure. To accomplish that, the number of farmers to be served by each field extension agent must be decided first, and then related to the average number of farms per square mile. Here, again, an arbitrary decision must be made. It appears that it is unrealistic to expect an extension worker to deal directly with more than about 400 farmers. If it is presumed that improved practices will spread among neighbors, a reasonable ratio may be one extension worker to 1200 farmers. With that decision made, the land area to be served by one unit of expansion can be calculated by taking into account the average number of farmers per square mile in the region under consideration.

How many miles of road will provide a reasonable network of farm-to-market roads for an IGP Area? We do not know with precision. But evidence from several countries suggests that, when completed, the minimum should be a road about every mile in one direction, connected by a crossroad about every three miles in the other, or a total of 1.34 miles of road per square mile of land.

Similar analyses can be made for each other task within the creation of the agri-support infrastructure, determining (by the application of criteria appropriate to each) the land area that can be served by each unit of expansion of each program activity.

(All of the decisions discussed so far with respect to program coefficients—extension workers and road mileage per square mile, etc.—and the analyses of activity characteristics should first be proposed by each agency of the ministry for its own activities. They should then be discussed with several agricultural development officers and the Office of Planning. Once determined, the analyses of activity characteristics and the quantitative coefficients should be used uniformly in all district and agency planning.)

IMPLEMENTATION PROFILES

In the book *Creating a Progressive Rural Structure*, where these procedures were described in greater detail, "Implementation Profiles" were suggested to show in graphic form the cost implications, over time, of an agricultural development plan based on these procedures. Each such profile can show at a glance what the cost implications of each program would be in terms of trained manpower, foreign exchange, and domestic expenditure during each stage (year) of its expansion.[29] After implementation profiles have been developed for separate programs, the same data can be used to show the cost implications of whatever combination of programs is being proposed, not only for the ensuing year but for future years of the Plan. This, in turn, facilitates revising the phasing of the Plan to avoid unacceptably wide variations in cost from year to year.

The procedures reviewed above are obviously only part of the analysis needed to answer the seven questions posed at the beginning of the chapter. They are discussed here, however, because, although elementary, they are so frequently omitted and estimates are based on little more than guesses. If a modern agriculture is to be created methodically and economically, the careful preparation of activity proposals is the first step.

---

[29] See examples of Implementation Profiles on pages 139-50 of *Creating a Progressive Rural Structure, op. cit.*

Chapter 8

MERGING GEOGRAPHIC, AGENCY AND NATIONAL CONSIDERATIONS

Not planning from the top down, nor from the bottom up, but a procedure that provides a feasible way to merge geographic, agency, and national considerations should be our goal.

Such a procedure would:

1. provide for district-by-district[30] planning that can serve both to enrich (without dominating) national planning and as a guide to local district initiative beyond the national plan;

2. give an active role in planning to major divisions of the ministry of agriculture, with each division helping plan the activities it subsequently will be responsible to implement;

---

[30] The districts referred to here are *farming districts* as defined in Chapter 1 and as discussed more fully in Chapter 2 of *Creating a Progressive Rural Structure, op. cit.,* pp. 13-30. As a practical matter, local or district planning will probably be done by present administrative districts, *kabupatens,* or "provinces." In most of South and Southeast Asia, "farming districts" of optimum size would range from 1500 to 2500 square miles in area, having an average radius fo 20 to 30 miles from the district headquarters market center. Whatever administrative unit comes closest to that size is probably the best unit to draw up "district" agricultural plans.

3. provide a method for injecting national priorities and restraints into the planning process during preliminary stages of agricultural planning within the ministry; and

4. provide a means for reconciling the conflicts and discrepancies among the above three initial inputs into the planning process.

Just to state these characteristics implies that many persons and agencies have important roles to play in agricultural planning. The relationships among agencies in planning are shown in broad outline in the chart on the following page. District plans need to be developed in and for each district. These district plans become an input into the planning activities of each major division of the ministry and of the Office of Integrated Projects, along with initial proposals generated by those agencies themselves. Meanwhile, the staff of the Office of Planning should prepare a statement of national considerations that indicate what priorities and constraints agricultural planning should take into account. The district and agency inputs should be brought together in consultative deliberations with the Office of Planning for revision, coordination and reconciliation. Out of these deliberations, the final proposals of the ministry for the Plan for Agriculture to the overall national planning body can be formulated by the full-time members of the Office of Planning, subject to approval by the minister.

DISTRICT PLANNING

The first task of district planning is to classify the lands of each district on the basis of growth potential: to locate each area of each type within the district. (A very rough approximation to such a classification can sometimes be made by the Office of Planning from secondary data, but it cannot give the detail of variations within each district that is needed for good planning. Such a broad-scale approximation may be useful in checking the classifications made by district planners but is inadequate taken alone.)

The second task of district planning is to propose appropriate

A PLANNING PROCESS FOR AGRICULTURE

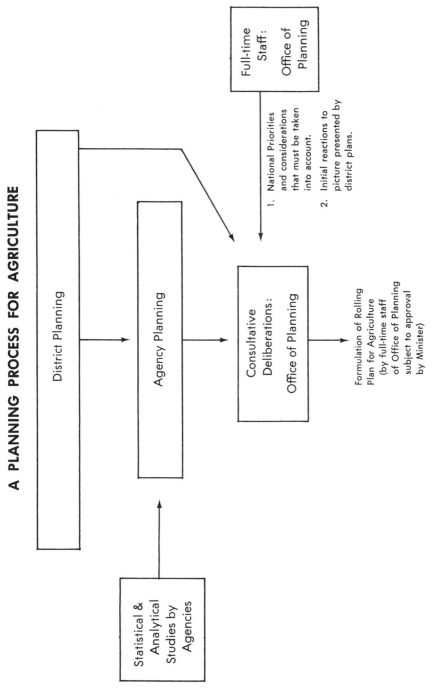

Full-time Staff:

Office of Planning

District Planning

Agency Planning

Statistical & Analytical Studies by Agencies

Consultative Deliberations: Office of Planning

1. National Priorities and considerations that must be taken into account.

2. Initial reactions to picture presented by district plans.

Formulation of Rolling Plan for Agriculture (by full-time staff of Office of Planning subject to approval by Minister) programs for the district, separately for each of its different classes of land from the standpoint of growth potential, and taking into account the twin goals of agricultural growth and rural welfare. District plans, as well as national plans, need to follow the "rolling plan" format, because much of what needs to be done in each district must be phased over a number of years if creating a modern agriculture is the goal. Each district plan needs to show not only the magnitude of each aspect of the total task but a manageable staging of implementation, year by year, until the goal is attained. Then, each year, this rolling plan can be revised to take account of what has been accomplished and of new opportunities that have emerged.[31]

It should be noted that the preparation of each district plan can, in addition to its contribution to national planning, have great utility locally. District authorities can frequently move ahead locally with aspects of their plan without waiting for national action. In the province of West Java, in Indonesia, a productivity tax is available to each district *(kabupaten)* for allocation to development purposes. In the Philippines, six governors of adjacent provinces have joined together to do their own planning and implementation. At a recent workshop on agricultural development twenty-five District Collectors in India emphasized that district initiative can often marshall local resources far beyond what the national Plan provides. Many opportunities like these exist, and the preparation of sound district plans is essential if they are to be exploited.

It is often useful to aggregate plans for several contiguous districts that lie within the same type-of-farming area, partly because individual IGP, FGP and LGP areas are seldom bounded by districts lines, but also to make comprehension of the overall problem easier at the national level. In deciding just how many districts to include in each regional plan, having the regions of

---

[31] A method of preparing district plans is outlined in *Creating a Progressive Rural Structure, op. cit.,* Appendix B, pp. 107-65.

equal size is much less important than having them reasonably homogeneous by dominant cropping patterns.

AGENCY PLANNING

The second major input into good agricultural planning is by the various public agencies related to agriculture, whether all of these are within the ministry of agriculture or not. In the remainder of this discussion it will be assumed that they are.

Agencies differ markedly in the degree to which they need to take district plans into account in drafting their proposals. Those that need to take district plans seriously into account include the various bureaus of the divisions of Research and of Rural Agri-Support Infrastructure, the Division of Manpower Training, and the various bureaus of the Division of Land Development. For example, the Extension Bureau should review all of the district requests to discern what volume and variety of extension activities they would require in the aggregate. The Bureau of Irrigation of the Division of Land Development should total the requests for irrigation construction, outline the magnitude of the task of undertaking technical feasibility studies for them, and estimate the cost of those projects on which preliminary studies are far enough along that early construction can seriously be considered. Similarly, each other bureau and division should estimate its own responsibility if all district requests were to be honored, and outline the program and the budget that would be required.

Following that, each agency should make an independent projection of what its own program should be in the coming year, taking into account but not being limited by district requests. In making that projection, the agency's primary criteria would be twofold. First, what is its own realistic expansion capacity, given the requirements of each activity for trained manpower and administrative supervision? Second, what are the agency's judgments as to where within the country the limited amount that can be done within the coming year should be located? The Division of Research may feel that it can only take on one or

99

two additional crops for intensive development even though district plans suggest that research on five new crops is needed. That alone may determine which areas of future growth potential within the country can effectively be served. Or the division may currently have personnel trained to work on one particular crop that is important in limited areas, but not competent to deal with a crop that is now grown over a much larger total area of future growth potential. In that case, the decision undoubtedly should be to work on the crop the division is now competent to deal with and to begin to develop or recruit competence to tackle the other crops of intrinsically higher priority a year or two hence.

In other words, while it is the function of district planning to identify needs and propose programs *it is the function of agency planning to judge feasibility and to propose orders of priority* based on both needs and feasibility.

The planning tasks of the divisions of Production Inputs and of Production Incentives are quite different. The impact of what they do is general, rather than being directly related to district activities. Plans of the Division of Production Inputs need to be related to what is happening in rural areas insofar as projections of probable demand for various farm inputs are concerned, but on the supply side those plans need to be closely integrated with activities of such ministries as industry, trade, and finance. The responsibility of the Division of Production Incentives requires that it keep abreast of relative farm prices and tenure patterns in different parts of the country, but its proposals for the most part have to do with policies that affect the whole country uniformly. Consequently, for both of these divisions, their input into planning consists primarily of programs and policies that *they* develop; district plans are less important to them.

The first-stage culmination of agency planning is a budget proposal from each division covering the nature of its proposed program for the coming year and the budget allocations that the program would require.

For the most part, each division budget can be made up by summation of budgets prepared by individual bureaus within it.

In some cases, however, *preliminary consultation among bureaus* must be part of the budget preparation process. This is particularly true in the Division of Rural Agri-Support Infrastructure since the expansion of credit and extension services and farm-to-market roads should be jointly rather than separately planned.[32] Moreover, the planning for integrated crop campaigns or other special projects by the Office of Integrated Projects requires preliminary consultations, because parts of each project will usually need to be implemented by different bureaus and should therefore be provided for in their separate budgets even though implementation is to be coordinated.

There is a difference among agencies as to how long into the future the "rolling plan" needs to be developed. The most important feature of each agency's plan is its proposals for the next ensuing year, because that becomes the basis for budgeting. Beyond that, some agencies may need to project their plans only a few years into the future (perhaps four or five years for Research or for the Division of Production Incentives.) On the other hand, the bureaus of Irrigation and Drainage may need to project their plans ten years ahead. It is unlikely that any agency needs to go to fifteen-year projections, as is advisable for district plans.

Criticisms. Two criticisms of these proposals with respect to district and agency planning need to be considered. One is that the suggested procedures are complicated. It is true that they are not simple, but it should not be difficult to follow them if appropriate operating procedures are adopted. One workable method would be for the Office of Planning, in consultation with agency and district officials, to work out standard forms for district plans, and then to have the completed district proposals returned to the Office of Planning. The Office of Planning would

---

[32] A special planning problem is presented in the case of farm-to-market roads. Extension of these roads should be closely coordinated with the expansion of other elements of a Progressive Rural Structure, yet such roads will almost invariably be the responsibility of a different ministry. Consequently, consultation at an early stage in the planning process each year between the appropriate bureau of that other ministry and the Division of Agri-Support Infrastructure is important.

then summarize and collate all district proposals in a manner that *retains the identity* of proposals for each district, and submit copies of these summaries to all interested agencies. In the beginning, when some but not all districts submit plans, or when those submitted vary greatly in quality, it would be important for all agencies to make allowances for those differences so that no district is penalized in the national plan just because the proposals submitted by its officers are inadequate.

The other criticism is that neither district officers nor agency officials in some countries are at present competent to do what would be required of them. Where that is true, the competence can be developed by a suitable program of in-service training. Participation of district and agency officers in planning is so important that it must not be foregone just because new types of competence have to be developed.

ROLES OF THE OFFICE OF PLANNING

So far we have discussed the role of district and agency officers in planning. What of the Office of Planning itself? Here we must consider separately the role of the full-time staff of the Office and the role of consultative deliberations involving the expanded group that includes representatives of all of the ministry's divisions and offices, of regional agricultural development officers, and of other ministries.

The full-time professional staff of a ministry of agriculture's Office of Planning has the primary and demanding task of being the translating and mediating agent among agricultural agencies, on the one hand, and between agricultural planning and overall national planning, on the other. In both of these mediating roles its primary allegiance must be to agriculture and its ministry. It must serve that allegiance, first, by serving as the interpreter and expositor of the major implications for agriculture of the objectives of the overall national plan and of the restraints that national circumstances impose on what can be done within the limits set by the nation's resources. It should serve it, secondly, by injecting its own critical judgments into the process of adjusting and reconciling the program proposals of different agricultural agencies. It should serve it, third, by translating the agricultural plan into categories that can be "plugged into" the national plan.

In carrying out these three responsibilities the full-time staff of the Office of Planning has important activities before, during, and after the enlarged consultative deliberations with representatives of districts and agencies.

Before those deliberations the staff should:

1. initiate district planning by preparing and sending out standard forms;
2. collate completed district plans for reference by agricultural agencies;
3. prepare and submit to all agencies its own comments after scanning the district plans; and
4. prepare and submit to all agencies a statement of national priorities and constraints that need to be taken into account.

During the consultative deliberations, the full-time staff should participate with all other members in discussing adjustments and alternative courses of action.

After the consultative deliberations the full-time staff has two tasks:

1. to work out final formulation of the proposed Plan for Agriculture, subject to approval by the minister; and
2. to translate the agricultural plan into a form in which it can be plugged into the process of overall national planning.

REVIEW OF DISTRICT AND AGENCY PROPOSALS

The full-time staff needs to bring to the review of district and agency proposals an overall perspective on the task of promoting agricultural growth and creating a modern agriculture that transcends the more limited viewpoints and interests of representatives of regions and of agencies. To do that it must have a deep understanding of the nature of agriculture and of the capabilities and limitations of public activities devoted to its development. It

103

must understand the complementarities among different public programs and between public and private activities. It must have an understanding of the importance of the sequences in which activities are launched and expanded, both nationally and within particular districts. Added to these, it must keep abreast of what is happening within the agricultural economy so that it can detect emerging problems as well as evaluate, in a general manner, the effectiveness of what has been done in the recent past and of what is being proposed for the future. In other words to perform this first function of providing a broad perspective plus a competence in critical review, members of the full-time staff need to be *specialists in agricultural development as a process* rather than being primarily specialists in techniques of macroeconomic analysis and manipulation. At the same time, in order to work effectively with the Planning Commission, at least some members of agriculture's Office of Planning need to be fully versed in macro-planning.

One criterion that is important in the overall review and adjustment of the Plan for Agriculture lies in the distinction between "seminal" and "induced" activities, coupled with an appreciation of the gestation periods of different activities before they begin to affect current production. Hayami and Ruttan have recently analyzed this distinction in presenting a "theory of induced development" for agriculture.[33] In essence, they contend that certain activities to promote agricultural growth will be "induced" if certain other activities are successfully undertaken first. The latter, or "seminal" activities are primarily those that develop new farm technology of a type appropriate and profitable in a given region. Hayami and Ruttan demonstrate historically that where such new technologies have been developed their availability has induced the initiation of the other activities that are necessary to exploiting the potential of the new technology. Professor Dantwala recently made the same point in his Presidential Address to the Indian Economics Association.

---

[33] Hayami and Ruttan, *op. cit.*

At the same time, Hayami and Ruttan point out (with less emphasis than it deserves) that several of these induced activities take a long time to develop. If the new technology makes irrigation profitable, it still takes years to design and construct major irrigation projects. Increasing commercialization of farming based on the new technologies may make a network of farm-to-market roads economic, but it may be several years before their construction is undertaken, and even then the construction of such a network takes a long time during which current production is impeded. Thus while it is important to distinguish between "seminal" and "induced" activities in order to make sure that the former get priority attention, it is also important (particularly where the rate of population growth is high) to take the gestation periods of other activities into account and to get started with those requiring a long gestation period without waiting for them to be "induced."

A second important task for the Office of Planning with respect to district and agency proposals is to review proposed programs as to the proportionality of their attention to areas of immediate, future and low agricultural growth potential, and with respect to their relative attention to agricultural growth and to rural welfare. It is important to move promptly toward creating or expanding a thoroughly modern agriculture in areas of immediate growth potential. It is important not to squander public expenditures trying to do that in areas not yet able to achieve it. It is important meanwhile to mount or strengthen those activities that are currently needed to raise at least some of the areas of future growth potential into the immediate high growth potential category.

With respect to each new program that is proposed the Office of Planning should ask: "Must this be a public activity, or could it be satisfactorily handled by the private sector, perhaps with suitable public stimulation and appropriate public policies?"

That question should be raised because of the need to get the most out of limited public resources. Taxation is a major method of accumulating savings in most countries of South and Southeast

105

Asia, while investment needs for activities that *must* be public far exceed them. Under these circumstances, every activity that can reasonably be left to private initiative, thereby stimulating private saving and investment, should be. Moreover, the administrative burden on each government is already great and should only be increased where absolutely necessary.

The question will not always be answered in the same way, but it should always be asked.

INTERPRETING NATIONAL PRIORITIES AND RESTRAINTS

The second role of the full-time members of the staff of the Office of Planning is to interpret national priorities and restraints to the representatives of regions and agencies who participate in the consultative deliberations of the office. These have to do primarily with five factors: (1) available trained manpower; (2) foreign exchange situation; (3) funds available for public expenditure; (4) repercussions on employment opportunities; and (5) current administrative capacity.

Trained manpower. One national restraint is the number of trained technicians competent to perform specific tasks. The kinds of competence required vary enormously. Not all of those engaged in agriculturally related tasks need to be trained in agriculture. Civil and mechanical engineers, business administrators, general economists and many other types of specialists are needed. Moreover, the possibilities of relatively brief preinduction training for specific tasks, and well administered in-service training, can produce competent personnel for many activities quite quickly. Nevertheless, the supply of trained manpower is a serious restraint in most countries and must be taken into account. Unless district and agency plans are reviewed with this in mind, it may be discovered late that several different proposed activities had anticipated using the same trained persons.

Foreign exchange situation. In general, measures to promote agricultural growth and to create a modern agriculture involve

106

relatively modest requirements for foreign exchange. Some scientific equipment, frequently some construction equipment, and perhaps the employment of technical consultants from abroad to substitute temporarily for domestically trained technicians in certain fields—these are the only requirements that may have to be met from abroad—*except* (and it may be a big exception) where farm production inputs must be imported. Fertilizers particularly, and to a lesser degree pesticides, may have to be imported and the total foreign exchange bill for these may become very high. The same may be true for farm equipment and tractors.

Increased farm production may considerably *decrease* the pressure on foreign exchange as a restraint either by allowing increased agricultural exports or by substituting for present imports of food or other agricultural products. The impact this has on agricultural planning may be to indicate prior attention to certain parts of the country, or to the production of certain crops,[34] because of their importance to the nation's balance of trade and foreign exchange position.

In any case, the balance-of-trade and foreign exchange situation is usually a national factor that must be taken into account in agricultural planning.

Magnitude of expendable public funds. The third national factor that must be taken into account in agricultural planning is the magnitude of expendable public funds, and the portion of those funds that may be allotted to agriculture. The better the organization of public agencies related to agriculture, and the better the arrangements for agricultural planning, the greater the capacity of the ministry of agriculture to utilize public funds effectively is likely to be. But the government has many other important demands on its resources also. Therefore, as capacity for good agricultural planning increases, the availability of public funds is likely to become a major restraint.

---

[34] Primarily through the nature of allocations for research and by actions with respect to farmers' production incentives.

In these circumstances, three considerations must be urged by the Office of Planning on all divisions and bureaus within the ministry. One is to take care not to undertake any activity that can be handled acceptably by the private sector. The second is to seek by every means possible to achieve high efficiency in all public activities. The third is to prepare program and budget proposals in such a way that they are adjustable to differing amounts of public expenditure that may become available, and to assure that necessary adjustments can take account of basic priorities as viewed by each agency and by the Office of Planning.

Available public revenues should seldom be a restraint on what is undertaken if the project or activity is really essential, and they should never be an excuse for so diluting the quality of an activity that it is ineffective. Instead, the impact of this restraint should determine how rapidly new activities can be launched and how soon the total need for them can be met.

Employment repercussions. The Office of Planning should insist that projected programs be analyzed from the standpoint of their impact on employment opportunities. This cannot be done with precision, and it will not be applicable to some aspects of the program. It *is* applicable to the program of the Division of Production Inputs, since some types of mechanization substitute for labor without raising productivity per acre. The test of employment repercussions is applicable also to the policy proposals of the Division of Production Incentives, since the increasing profitability of farming may set off changes in farm size that reduce employment opportunities. It is particularly applicable to the technology proposed for constructing and maintaining roads and irrigation facilities, because a choice can often be made between labor-intensive and capital-intensive methods of accomplishing the same results in the construction and maintenance of these facilities.

Current administrative capacity. Activities vary widely in the kind and quality of administration that are essential to their success. Price control programs are a good example of activities that, however desirable, may involve administrative problems that cannot effectively be handled. Many credit programs have failed for the same reason. Some activities that have been effective on a small scale fall apart when efforts are made to expand them rapidly. Current administrative capacity is a restraint that must be respected if resources are not to be wasted.

PLANNING BY "CONSULTATIVE DELIBERATIONS"

After district and agency proposals have been prepared, and national priorities and restraints have been "placed on the table," the time has come for the plan to be put together. This can only be done by a process of trial and retrial until a feasible plan emerges. The participants in this process should include staff members of the Office of Planning, representatives of each division of the ministry of agriculture, representatives of major agricultural regions, and consultative members from related ministries. (See chart on page 69.)

Critical review of agency proposals. It is here that the proposals of each of the participating groups are critically examined, both in themselves and in relation to each other. That examination should not be just in terms of proposed expenditures; instead it should be in terms of *what* each agency proposes to do, *in what manner* it proposes to do it, *where* in the country each activity is to be carried on, and whether the timing of each activity is appropriate in the light of the current growth potential of different parts of the country, complementarities among activities, and the various gestation periods that are involved.

Adjustment and reconciliation of agency proposals. The second task of consultative deliberations is to adjust and reconcile agency proposals into a plan for agriculture. Having the initial proposals made by agencies, reviewing district plans and injecting their own technical judgment, should assure the availability of soundly conceived projects and programs. At the same time,

109

it means that those projects and programs emanate from specialists who may not have taken important factors into account. Even if they have, resources may not be adequate to allow all of the proposed programs to be provided for at the full strength at which they are recommended.

It should not be inferred that the consultative deliberations during which the major decisions with respect to the agricultural plan are discussed should occur only once, after which the full-time staff of the Office of Planning would formulate the Plan for approval by the minister. Instead, these consultations should take place at least three times, and perhaps more.

The first occasion would be when the representatives of regional agricultural development officers and of the various divisions and offices of the ministry (including the full-time members of the Office of Planning) present their initial proposals. At that time the discrepancies, conflicts, and overall balance would be fully discussed and proposals for modification suggested.

The second occasion would be after suggested modifications have been formulated when, again, all members would have an opportunity to comment and recommend further modifications.

The third occasion should be after the Rolling Plan for Agriculture has been drafted by the full-time members of the Office of Planning but before it has been approved by the minister.

The minister should himself be present at all these sessions so that he knows at first hand what the various inputs have been and what the discussions have revealed. He should not come in just at the final stage. He should not be dependent on what the chief of the Office of Planning tells him about the arguments that have been raised in the process of formulating the Plan.

TRANSLATING THE AGRICULTURAL PLAN INTO MACRO-CATEGORIES

After the agricultural plan that is to be proposed to the national overall planning agency has been agreed upon, its features must be translated into the macro-categories that will allow it to mesh with other sectors of the national plan. This task falls to the full-time staff of agriculture's Office of Planning.

The first task is to separate those projected expenditures that would require foreign exchange from those that can be met by domestic currency.

The second is to make an estimate of the extent to which proposed expenditures actually constitute investment and to what extent they are "public costs of current production."[35] That is difficult even to estimate, and nothing but an estimate is possible. Yet it is important because the rate of investment is of major concern in overall economic planning. The distinction between investments, public costs of current production and adjustment costs (that may or may not include overt "transfer payments") normally will not appear explicitly in program proposals initiated by district officers or by agricultural agencies. Consequently, it falls to the Office of Planning to make the distinction and then to consider critically whether the relationships among them seem reasonable, both for individual activities and in the aggregate.

The third task in translating a plan for agriculture into macrocategories is to estimate the impact of the total plan and of each major aspect of it on employment, both farm and non-farm, rural and urban.

---

[35] See Appendix C, page 144.

Chapter 9

JUDGING PROPORTIONALITY
AMONG MAJOR ACTIVITIES

Carefully analyzing each proposed activity as proposed in Chapter 7 can result in a reasonably precise estimate of physical requirements, unit costs, and time requirements of tasks essential to creating a modern agriculture. They are important to orderly planning and implementation and to adjusting activities to available resources. What they do not do is to relieve us of the necessity of making qualitative decisions when it comes to deciding how much of available resources to spend on research, how much on procuring production inputs, how much on the agri-support infrastructure, how much on increasing production incentives, how much on land development, and how much on training agricultural technicians.

These must be qualitative decisions for two reasons. First, and most important, the proportions in which resources should be allocated to these six major activities depend primarily on the differing situation in various parts of the country, how much of the structure of a modern agriculture has been achieved in each district, and what activities with long gestation periods need to be launched or expanded promptly if the facilities they will make available are to be ready when needed.

Second, although we can estimate costs, and the land area over which specified activities will make certain facilities available, we cannot similarly estimate *benefits* in the form either of agricultural production or rural welfare with any comparable precision. Activities vary enormously in quality depending on how they are conducted. The actual use that will be made of facilities that are provided cannot be predicted. There are large uncertainties about the outcome of activities such as research and public expenditures to improve production incentives, and of course, it is impossible to quantify the value of improvement in certain aspects of human welfare.

Research can have a high payoff if it is well administered, properly focussed on high priority problems, and manned by scientists of high quality and imagination. But it can be a costly waste if, as frequently happens, it does not have these characteristics. Universities can bring a high return if their curricula are geared to a country's needs, if their professors are competent, if their students are diligent and imaginative, and if their graduates actually stay in the fields for which they are trained. But much of the money spent on universities can be, and often is, largely wasted because they do not meet one or more of these tests.

What this situation requires is that every activity supported by public funds be carefully analyzed for indications of the quality of the contribution it makes to the public it serves, and that this scrutiny be frequently repeated.

If we give proper attention to *sequences, gestation periods,* and *complementarities* we can be reasonably certain that expenditures on the various major activities will move us *in the direction of* creating a modern agriculture, but we cannot do better than to make qualitative judgments about the most effective proportionality among these activities, year by year.

There are, to be sure, mathematical techniques that are often used in connection with planning. *They are much more widely applicable in economies that are already wholly commercial and modernized,* and they may be more useful in industrial than in agricultural planning. But in a country that is in the process of modernizing its agriculture, their applicability is more limited. They can be used at certain preliminary stages but not at the crucial final point of allocations among major components of an agricultural plan that takes the nature of agriculture and the nature of the process of agricultural growth into account.

Cost/benefit analysis, for example, can be useful in analyzing the probable rate of return on some types of projects (such as major irrigation works). More specifically, an honest cost/benefit analysis can tell us when *not* to engage in a project because of high cost relative to probable returns, but it cannot tell us *to* undertake a project at a particular time if the same resources might be put to other uses. That is because there are other activities important to agricultural growth for which comparable cost/benefit analyses cannot be calculated. Those who are competent in cost/benefit analysis know this, and they know that final allocative decisions are always made by one or another form of consultative deliberation or administrative decision, informed (perhaps) by cost/benefit studies but not limited by them, even within planning commissions.

Input/output analysis relates output of a given commodity to given amounts of specific inputs of homogeneous quality, or, at a more aggregative level, it relates the output of an industry to given amounts of various inputs used by it. It is a very useful tool for analyzing relationships within a given firm, industry or economy at a given point in time. But it assumes a given state of the arts and a given form of organization whereas the core problem in creating a modern agriculture is to *change* the state of the arts and to *change* the form of organization of the agricultural industry, developing new agri-support services and constantly improving their quality.[36]

---

[36] As Waterston put it, in his book *Development Planning: Lessons of Experience, op. cit.,* "Unlike anti-cyclical planning, development planning cannot assume implementation through existing institutions . . . [that] already operate with accept-

The case for linear programming is similar. It can establish an optimum solution where there is a choice among several alternative ways of reaching a defined objective, subject to certain definable constraints and when the contribution of each of the inputs is predictable and certain. But it is not adapted to performing that function where the quality of individual inputs is uncertain within a considerable range (such as not knowing just what the production effect of a given amount of money spent on administering a credit program will be).

Mathematical models that simulate an economy or the agricultural sector of it can be useful in giving an overview of how an economy works and of what changes in performance might be expected if certain features of it were modified in certain ways. In this sense it is more useful for agricultural planning purposes than input/output analysis because it can estimate the effects of selected *changes* within a certain order of magnitude. But it cannot, with confidence, derive precise coefficients that can be fed into an allocative equation embodying all of the major activities on which creating a modern agriculture depends.[37] Again, its most competent practitioners know this.

Consequently, when we conclude that allocative decisions in agricultural planning must be made by consultative deliberation, using the best that we can devise in the way of guidelines, we are not proposing that procedure as a substitute for a feasible mathematical alternative; instead, we are relying on the only appropriate method available to us.

It should be understood that the foregoing comments with respect to the limitations of mathematical techniques apply *only* to their usefulness in allocating resources among the six major components of public agricultural activity stressed throughout this

---

able efficiency." Instead, building new implementing institutions or improving old ones must be part of the substance of development planning. Input/output analysis cannot encompass this part of the development process.

See also, Appendix D, page 148.

[37] Myrdal examines this topic analytically in *Asian Drama*, Vol. 3, Appendix 3, pp. 1941-68. See also his critique of the use of capital/output ratios, beginning on page 1968.

book. The reasons for classifying public activities into those six components are implicit in the nature of agriculture as an industry and were explained further in chapters 3 and 5. The mathematical techniques commented on, however, were developed to meet specific needs in wholly commercial and largely industrialized economies where the quality of inputs is much more homogeneous, stimulating *changes* in the state of the arts is not part of the problem, nor is the development of and choice among new institutions and forms of organization so important.

Mathematical techniques can be extremely useful even now and with respect to selected agricultural problems in south and southeast Asia. But their usefulness is in research, in various types of analytical study, rather than in making final major allocations in agricultural planning. They therefore need to be part of the "kit of tools" of economists in a ministry of agriculture's Division of Research and in universities. They can "tighten up sloppy thinking," reveal unsuspected assumptions, and lead to valuable insights when they are correctly used.

In planning, the proportions in which allocations are made among the six components should be a *resultant* of district and agency planning and the "consultative deliberations" described earlier. Those resulting proportions will be influenced by:

1. the relative proportions of the country's agricultural land that now lies in IGP, FGP and LGP Areas;
2. what has been accomplished and what remains to be done, district by district;
3. the relative costliness of the different tasks that need to be undertaken now; and
4. the relative importance ascribed to each of the five objectives listed at the beginning of Chapter 6.

The proportions in which resources should be allocated to the six major components of creating a modern agriculture should therefore differ from country to country and from year to year in the same country.

Chapter 10

SUMMARY: REQUIREMENTS FOR SOUND AGRICULTURAL PLANNING

T hroughout this book the emphasis has been on organization and planning to create a modern agriculture. It should be clear by now that the considerations bearing on the two topics—organization and planning—interact to such an extent that they need to be considered together. Those interactions are reflected in the extent to which considerations of organization come into this chapter, the purpose of which is to draw together the implications of what has been presented throughout the book with respect to agricultural planning.

Recall that our concern is about that particular period when creating a modern agriculture has become a feasible immediate objective in at least some parts of each country, but when the task has not yet been completed. Later on, other forms of organization and planning may become preferable, but to shift to those now would result in practices that would not serve the immediate task of *creating* a modern agriculture satisfactorily. And even though creating a modern agriculture should be the primary concern during this period, other tasks are simultaneously important, so agricultural planning should include attention to them as well.

1. *Planning to create a modern agriculture must include attention to both technological and institutional changes.*

The goal is a radically different kind of agriculture from that which each country has had in the past. This new type of agriculture involves new methods of farming, a changed organization of the countryside, and new forms of local and national organizations and policies.

A modern agriculture is one in which even the plants and livestock are of different types from those previously grown. It is one in which purchased farm inputs are of infinitely greater importance. It is one in which practices of husbandry are very different. It is one in which off-farm agri-support services that previously were not needed must be developed and operated and assume major importance. It is one in which the quality of the land itself is changed to become the base for a more productive agriculture. It is one where either diversified and constantly shifting combinations of enterprises or continuous specialized production are possible, in response to changing relative prices. Several of these taken together require a new overall organization of the countryside, and new interrelationships among farms, market towns and cities, and between agriculture and industry.

These major transformations involve both technological and institutional changes. Some of the needed technological changes affect methods of farm production: new crop varieties, new pest control materials, new implements, new sources of power. Some provide new methods of marketing, storing, transporting and processing farm products. Still others affect the methods of producing and distributing farm inputs.

The institutional changes that are involved include new organizational arrangements for agricultural research and for training agricultural technicians, new ways of extending credit to farmers, new patterns of operation for organizations that market farm products and that distribute farm inputs, arrangements for influencing farmers' production incentives, sometimes for changing patterns of land tenure and tenancy and frequently new methods of arranging for the management of irrigation systems.

They need to include changes in how ministries of agriculture are organized and operated and a distinctive method for agricultural planning itself.

Expenditures on all of these types of changes constitute investments, since they expand the opportunities for future agricultural production. Some of those investments are in physical facilities, while many others are costs of establishing new organizations or modernizing the operation of old ones. Consequently, agricultural planning must involve much more than providing for investments in physical facilities; it must provide for the full range of technological and institutional changes that are required to create a modern agriculture.

Another way of stating these requirements is that creating a modern agriculture involves improving the *quality* of most inputs, not just increasing the quantity of them devoted to agriculture. That is true not just of agricultural research to improve the quality of individual inputs ranging from seeds through implements and cultural practices to power units. It is true also of credit institutions, marketing facilities, tax collection procedures, and administrative procedures.

2. *Planning should embrace all public activities related to agriculture: production, growth and adjustment.*

During the period when a modern agriculture is being created, agricultural growth should be the primary goal. But attention must also be given, even within that period, to those parts of the agricultural production process that need to be conducted as public activities, and to needed adjustments within agriculture and between agriculture and other parts of the economy. To fail to make proper provision for activities like seed certification, policing of market grades and standards, and public attention to crop and livestock pest and disease control would be to fail to take advantage of the already existing capacity for agricultural production. Likewise, attention to the special problems of small farmers, to growing disparities between the incomes of farmers in different parts of the country and between farm operators and laborers in the same regions cannot safely be delayed. A reasonable degree of political stability is important to current production, and an acceptable pattern of income distribution should be a major goal of public policy in any case, quite apart from its relevance to agricultural growth.

All three roles of public agricultural programs—production, growth, and adjustment—have to be financed out of public revenues. The programs of the same public agencies frequently serve two or even all three functions. Consequently, agricultural planning needs to cover all activities that serve any one of the three purposes.

3. *Effective agricultural planning requires an appropriate specification of the "activities" among which resources are to be allocated.*

It is not feasible to plan separately for technological and institutional changes, since both are involved in individual programs. It is not feasible to plan separately with respect to production, growth and adjustment for the same reason. It is not helpful to make the divisions in either organization or planning along the lines of academic disciplines, even though that is frequently done.

Some principle or principles must be given more weight than others in determining what lines the division into "activities" is to follow. In the proposals made here, two principles are predominant. The most important is to give the needs for agricultural growth and for creating a modern agriculture the greatest weight. The other is to select a set of activities that can serve simultaneously for organization and planning so that planning, budgeting and implementation can be linked together effectively and in a straightforward manner.

It is in line with these considerations that it has been proposed that the total task should be divided into six major components or "activities."

1. *Agricultural research*
2. *Provision of farm inputs*

3. *Rural agri-support infrastructure*
4. *Influencing farmers' production incentives*
5. *Land development*
6. *Training agricultural technicians*

With these six being the major activities for agricultural planning, one can be sure that all of the components for creating a modern agriculture are taken into account in a way that allows direct and implementing linkages. With each of the same six being the responsibility of a major division of the ministry of agriculture, one has a form of organization for that ministry that is focused primarily on creating a modern agriculture, and that closely relates planning, budgeting, and implementation.

4. *Sound allocative planning for agriculture requires disaggregation of certain activities in accord with the varying current agricultural growth potential of different parts of the country.*

Public agricultural planning has to do primarily with agri-support activities and with the agri-milieu.

Measures to change the agri-milieu normally affect the whole country uniformly because it is difficult, politically, to apply public policies regarding such matters as taxation, prices, and land tenure differentially in different parts of the country. The same policies must be applied equally everywhere within the country.

However, the situation is different with respect to agri-support activities. Three clusters of these, in particular, need to be analyzed with respect to the urgency of the need for each in different parts of the country and its consequent profitability if established in those places. These are:

1. The Rural Agri-Support Infrastructure;
2. Agricultural Research; and
3. Land Development.

The key to the most effective deployment of these activities is to disaggregate them in accord with the differing growth potential of different areas within the country. To provide a complete rural agri-support infrastructure is economically defensible only in IGP Areas, areas of immediate growth potential.[38] Meanwhile, priority attention should be given in FGP Areas to research or land development, or both, as circumstances may warrant, in order to raise those areas into the IGP category.

To put the matter another way, *a modern agriculture is an objective that is reached geographical area by geographical area;* it is not an objective that is reached crop by crop, nor is it achieved agri-support activity by activity. It is achieved farming locality by locality, and for each locality what it is important to do each year through public programs and policies depends on whether that locality has an immediate, a future, or a low potential for agricultural growth, as well as on what agri-support activities have already been established there.

It is not a disaggregation of planning by administrative or farming districts that is required, although district planning is part of the process. The appropriate procedure may approach disaggregation by districts to the extent that entire districts may fall largely within a single category of either immediate, future, or low growth potential. Most districts are not so uniform, however, so separate attention to areas of immediate, future, and low growth potential will cut across district lines.

Neither should agricultural planning be along commodity lines. It is misleading to think of agriculture as rice plus wheat plus cotton plus sugarcane, etc., as a basis for planning for growth. Instead, it is important to conceive agriculture as being made up of thousands or millions of *farm businesses* of various sizes and types, producing different commodities in various proportions, using various technologies in the process, and lying within farming localities having very different growth potentials in the near future. Farmers do the production planning, taking into account the fixed resources of their land, the purchasable inputs con-

---

[38] Research should be continued with respect to IGP Areas in order to increase options for the future. Further land development may also be economic.

veniently available to them, and the signals they get from prices and from other sources of information.[39]

One point among many others at which the basis for disaggregation is particularly important is in estimating the near-future requirements for farm production inputs. If the disaggregation is by commodities, there is a strong temptation to set production targets for particular farm products and then to deduce from those targets the amount of different farm inputs that will be needed. That procedure guarantees neither that the production targets will be met nor that effective demand for the inputs and the supply of them provided will be approximately equal. Instead, it is much better to make arrangements for gathering information regularly each year about the volume of sales of each input by wholesalers in each district, from these to calculate the trend in the amounts farmers are purchasing each year, and then to extrapolate the probable effective demand in the near and in the more distant future, region by region and in the aggregate.[40] This is likely to lead to a closer equilibration of demand and available supply;[41] it yields information on the adequacy of regional storage facilities; it does not tie input procurement practices to the highly

[39] Perhaps it bears repeating that this method of planning does not prevent a subsidiary type of commodity planning that can be very useful. If agricultural growth is the overriding objective, commodity planning is only pertinent in areas of immediate growth potential in any case; in other areas it could only substitute the production of one crop for that of another and in an uneconomic manner, because it can be assumed that farmers are already growing different crops in the proportions that technologies available to them make most profitable. By definition, it is only in areas of immediate growth potential that more profitable technologies are currently available. While using the land classification according to growth potential as the basis for disaggregative planning, priority can still be given to those areas of immediate growth potential that produce a particular crop that the government wants to push, either to improve a balance of trade or foreign exchange situation or to increase the quantity of a particular farm product for domestic consumption.

[40] With due adjustment for any predictable changes in relative prices caused by changes in governmental price or subsidy policies.

[41] But a country intent on agricultural growth should not be too eager to have the supply of and the demand for farm inputs be evenly balanced. Instead, it should plan on always having some excess supply so that no farmer is ever prevented from using purchased inputs because stocks have been depleted.

uncertain results of trying to predict future production of particular commodities.

Meanwhile, while using extrapolated recent trends to determine the quantities of production inputs that should be supplied, it is useful to conduct analytical studies of the factors responsible for recent trends because of the insights these studies might yield as to how the use of production inputs can be accelerated. Such studies can be conducted by universities or by the Division of Research.

5. *Agricultural planning should utilize sequences, gestation periods and complementarities as criteria in making allocations, rather than separately estimated rates of return.*

Honoring both sequences and gestation periods is inherent in disaggregation on the basis of growth potentials; honoring complementarities is a major factor in treating all aspects of a rural agri-support infrastructure as a single planning "activity."

These three criteria need to be kept in mind and applied in other ways as well. For example, research and the training of research workers are highly complementary, whether in universities or in research institutes. They are so complementary that they should almost always be combined. Similarly, conducting extension activities and supervising local verification trials are so complementary that it may be well to have them conducted by the same bureau in addition to having them in the same division.

The gestation period for training technicians to perform certain tasks is so much longer in the context of college training than in in-service training that it should be entrusted to the latter much more widely than it now is.

On the negative side, separately estimated rates of return are inadequate allocative criteria partly because of the impossibility of calculating such rates for separate activities or projects with precision. The complementarities among them are too high to permit separate calculation of benefits. And benefits vary enormously depending on the effectiveness with which a given amount of expenditure is utilized in each activity or project.

126

There is an additional complication in trying to make allocative decisions on the basis of separate rates of return for each activity. Agricultural growth depends on a number of different activities, some private and some public, that are needed in certain physical quantities in relation to each other regardless of the individual costs of each. To return to an analogy used earlier, an automobile needs three or four wheels, one engine block, one engine cooling system, one generator, and the choice between one or two carburetors is based on operating efficiency of the total engine rather than on how much carburetors cost to manufacture. No matter how costly generators may be, one must be a part of each car; a fifth wheel or a second cooling system cannot substitute for it. And how much it pays to spend on the generator depends on the quality of the generator both intrinsically and in relation to the quality of all other components. It is the quality of each component and the complementarities among them that determine how much it is rational to spend on each.

The situation is similar with respect to creating a modern agriculture. An analysis of the relative costs (if not cost/benefit ratios) of different alternative ways of going about a particular activity can frequently be very helpful in choosing among possible methods. But when it comes to making allocations *among* activities of different types, the factors to consider are appropriate sequences, gestation periods, and complementarities, with attention to the quality of each activity always being important.

6. *Planning should focus on systematically building the structure of a modern agriculture,* taking advantage of emerging opportunities to increase production quickly but not allowing planning to be dominated by them.

This principle is pivotal to the entire argument of this book.

In an earlier period, after disillusionment brought on by the failure of single-emphasis "panacea" programs to produce adequate results, but before the high-yielding cereals were introduced in Asia, it became generally accepted that a productive agriculture is a complicated system, each part of which is important.

127

Then when the new varieties became available the pendulum swung toward the view that new higher-yielding technology is the crucial requirement. This near return to a much earlier view was tempered only by recognition that farmers must have adequate economic incentives and that, therefore, price and/or subsidy policies are also important.

What was glossed over in this recent trend in thinking was the fact that the new cereal technologies have led to substantial production increases only in areas where a good start had already been made in providing various agri-support services. The new wheats spread rapidly in that part of Mexico where, for thirty years, substantial investments had been made in irrigation and in roads, and where market towns offering a wide variety of farm inputs were already flourishing. They spread in those parts of the Punjab of India and Pakistan where irrigation and a network of roads had been in place for at least fifty years, and where farmers had been growing crops for sale and even for export for almost that long, with the result that marketing and credit facilities, and outlets for farm inputs were well-established.

A major spurt in production can be brought on by any one of several new developments, provided all of the other requirements are already in place.

We must not forget that similarly spectacular increases in production have occurred before, and that not all of those spurts were triggered by a new crop variety. A few years ago, there was a sudden rise in production in northeast Thailand, triggered by the opening of a major highway that increased the convenience and lowered the cost of transportation, coinciding with an expanded demand in Japan for imported feed grains. Still earlier, similar spurts in production occurred in West Africa in response to a market in Europe for cocoa, and in the Punjab in response to newly installed irrigation systems. *It is the last essential element to be added that usually gets the credit.*

The significance of this history is that spurts in production are to be expected, from time to time, and the triggering element will not always be the same. What the "triggering" element is will depend on what other essential facilities have already been developed during periods when they did not result in substantial immediate increases in production.

Consequently, knowing that several different elements are essential if a modern agriculture is to be achieved, it is wise to keep working on them, not haphazardly or equally at all times but selectively, guided by annually up-dated analyses of the growth potential of each part of the country and taking into account which elements are already reasonably adequate and which ones are lagging behind, locality by locality.

This principle does not invalidate the Hayami-Ruttan distinction between seminal and induced activities but seeks to put it in perspective. It is generally true that new farm technology appropriate to a region's resource base will induce development of the other facilities and policies that are essential to its profitable use. But it may take a long time. How far it will pay for a country to go in organizing and planning along lines suggested here should depend on what time lag the country feels it can afford; probably not very long, in view of present rates of population growth and levels of unemployment.

Given the new technologies now available, and the substantial research facilities now in place and contemplated for the near future, it would seem wise, even while continuing a major emphasis on research, to proceed with systematically building the structure of a modern agriculture in all IGP Areas but not elsewhere. Meanwhile in FGP Areas, appropriate activities to raise them to the IGP classification should be undertaken.

Emerging opportunities for spurts in production can be exploited as they arise by integrated commodity campaigns in IGP Areas, but their success should not be misinterpreted as signs that achievement of a modern agriculture has been completed. They are not.

7. *Those who participate in agricultural planning must understand the nature of agriculture and the process of agricultural growth.*

129

process which is itself, in the last analysis, political because of the important role that consultative deliberations must play. The Plan may still, of course, be modified after it leaves the ministry, but the distinction is between ministry formulation and external subsequent changes; the distinction is not between good agricultural planning and political considerations.

Part IV

Postscript

MOVING TOWARD THE MODEL

The fact that the proposals made herein with respect to organization and planning constitute a "normative model" has already been mentioned. In introducing Chapter 4, it was assumed that an opportunity was to arise completely to reorganize a ministry of agriculture. But that opportunity very seldom actually comes. Meanwhile, what can be done? Repeatedly, in discussions of these chapters, the question has been raised: What can we do that might be less than ideal but better than what we have now?

Whether this is a reasonable question to try to answer depends on what is back of it. Changes in either governmental organization or planning procedures are undoubtedly difficult to bring about. But what right do governmental officials have to ask farmers to change patterns of tenancy, or consolidate holdings, or reform cooperative societies if they are unwilling or unable to bring about similarly drastic changes in their own ways of operation? If the rate of agricultural growth is really affected by the forms of organization of public activities and by planning procedures, then changes of whatever magnitude are needed ought to be made and we should not be looking for easier compromise solutions.

However, there is a way to rephrase the question that would make it highly relevant. That would be to ask, not how can we get by without making the changes we should, but how can we get started toward a goal we would like to reach? For major changes can frequently be accomplished step by step, and some countries have, in fact, already begun.

A COORDINATING COUNCIL FOR AGRICULTURE

Where there are a number of independent agricultural agencies outside the ministry of agriculture, one way of securing some coordination (short of bringing them back into the ministry) is to establish a coordinating council of which the minister and the chief administrative officer of each independent agency are members. Such a council—and several have been established—can at least establish frequent communication among the member agencies. It could even take the set of six major activities that have been emphasized in this book as its agenda headings for periodic reviews of what is being done. It could formulate proposals for inclusion in future plans by whatever agency may now be formulating plans. As it identifies weak or blank spots in current activities, it could recommend changes and new activities to be undertaken either by one of its member agencies or by another ministry.

One problem inherent in trying to rely permanently on such a council is that the existing pattern of agencies is not likely to correspond to the six major activities. Responsibilities with respect to certain activities may be divided among two or more agencies, while other important activities are now no one's responsibility. Another problem is that if "independent" agencies are really independent, no one except a president or prime minister is in a position to force real coordination and he is too busy with other matters to be able to do that effectively.

Colombia recently introduced a system that comes close to the pattern presented in this book, although the "activities" are differently defined. It has set up *all* public agricultural activities as independent agencies, but all such agencies are responsible to the Minister for Agriculture. The Ministry itself is quite small and performs only a coordinating role; it directly administers no programs.

A New Structure for Planning for Agriculture by General Planning Commissions

Where planning for agriculture is done by a general planning commission, that commission could adopt a method of planning for agriculture similar to that proposed here. It could adopt the six recommended major activities for purposes of planning. It could institute a system for getting district plans prepared, including the delineation of IGP, FGP and LGP Areas, and use these district plans in its plan formulation. It could recommend a realignment of agricultural agencies, or the creation of new ones, in order to get a better fit between each element of its plan and a single organization for implementing it.

District Planning

District planning can be initiated without waiting for emergence of a new national pattern of organization and planning. Such district plans can be very useful locally, since administrative units other than national governments often have resources they can devote to developmental purposes. In addition, district officials can often influence where in their districts particular national activities are undertaken. They can thus achieve more efficient utilization of national resources locally, even though other districts may not be following the same procedures. This is being done now in a few places in Indonesia, the Philippines, and India, although in a different manner in each country.

An Agricultural Policy Panel in the Ministry of Agriculture

Even without reorganizing the agencies within a ministry of agriculture, the minister could set up a special staff panel to advise him on agricultural policy, and that panel could utilize the categories of activities proposed in this study in carrying out its task. Such a panel should not limit its studies to activities administered by the ministry but should take into account all of the agri-support services, public or private, that are needed, as well as considering appropriate programs or policies to affect the agri-milieu.

To be effective, the panel should have three or more full-time members, with a director or executive secretary responsible only to the minister and having right of access to information and data from all agencies within the ministry.

Insofar as activities administered by the ministry are concerned, this panel could serve as an Office of Planning for the ministry. In developing plans, the panel could encourage district planning; it could involve all agencies within the ministry in studying district plans and making their own program proposals; it could utilize consultative deliberations in refining its proposals. The minister could then recommend the proposals developed by the panel to the general planning commission for consideration.

Even if it did not engage in formal planning, such a panel could be of great help to the minister of agriculture in performing his complicated and difficult role. Actually a minister of agriculture has three important roles to play. As a bare minimum he must be a competent *administrator* of the programs entrusted to his ministry. Beyond that, since many programs and policies affecting agriculture are administered or initiated by other ministries and by independent agencies the minister of agriculture has a responsibility to serve as an *Ambassador for Agriculture*, representing agriculture's interests in dealing with agencies outside of his ministry and with the legislature. Third, it is most helpful if he can, in addition, be a *Statesman for Agriculture*, seeing its present problems in a broad context, foreseeing its future problems, and seeking to influence public opinion as well as other administrators and legislators.

No man can fill all three of these roles competently by relying on his own knowledge and experience alone. Instead, he must preside over a whole set of investigative processes from which he can constantly be learning. An effective way to provide this support would be to adopt a pattern of organization and planning similar to the one proposed in earlier chapters. In the absence of such arrangements, a Panel on Agricultural Policy, responsible to him, could be very helpful.

Coordination of Activities to Develop a Progressive Rural Structure

A move in the right direction but on a narrower front would be to begin to coordinate those public activities that form integral parts of a Progressive Rural Structure. District planning does this at the local level. Similarly, a minister could set up a coordinating committee composed of the directors of extension services, credit agencies, and any activities the ministry has related to marketing and/or the distribution of farm inputs. He might even be able, without too much difficulty, to appoint a Director of Agri-Support Infrastructure over the directors of those relevant established agencies of the ministry to give continuing attention to their co-ordination in both implementation and planning.

Establish Ministry Agencies of Production Inputs and of Farmers' Incentives

These two major divisions proposed for a ministry of agriculture are not represented by any agencies in most ministries at the present time. In some cases it might be possible to get them authorized and established before it becomes feasible to make other recommended organizational changes.

Arrange for Training in Development Planning

If personnel of a ministry of agriculture are to participate in planning, they must learn how to do it. The procedures suggested in this book would require the full-time services of some persons as staff-members of the Office of Planning and the part-time services of a larger number of specialist technicians in all public agricultural agencies. All would need training in the procedures involved, with each procedure suitably modified to meet the special needs of each country.

Even before any other steps have been taken by ministries or by planning commissions, a ministry or a university might organize discussion-seminars to criticize the ideas reviewed in this book, inviting selected governmental administrators, planners, and members of budget bureaus to participate. Such seminars might be followed at later dates by training programs for much larger groups to familiarize them with whatever procedures it may be found useful to adopt in each country. The results of the seminars could also be used by universities in revising their academic courses on development planning.

❖   ❖   ❖

Any one of these steps might be undertaken alone, or different ones of them could be undertaken simultaneously. None of them precludes any of the others. Which one or ones should be taken first will depend on which are most acceptable at the time and on the availability of competent staff to undertake them. All of them can help move in the direction of achieving types of organization and planning that give primary attention to creating a modern agriculture and that make a close interaction among planning, budgeting and implementation possible.

Appendix A

PUBLIC OR PRIVATE OPERATION OF
COMMERCIAL AGRI-SUPPORT ACTIVITIES

The multiplication and distribution of improved seeds, the manufacture and distribution of fertilizer, pesticides, farm equipment
and implements, and the provision of farm production credit are
all agri-support services for which farm operators can be expected to pay as they are used. Consequently, these agri-support
activities are amenable to private operation. In some countries, at
certain stages of development, they have all been privately managed. However, there are two reasons why, in most countries,
public management of one or more of them has been introduced,
with or without trying to prevent private management as well.

One reason is that commercial agri-support services can be
monopolized, either by large firms or by collusion among many
small private firms, to the disadvantage of farm operators. The
other is that commercial agri-support services tend to be set up in
such a way that large farm operators have more access to them
than small farmers, and in such a way that they are most acces-
sible in areas of prosperous and already modern farming. Thus

they tend to follow rather than to promote the process of modernization.

The argument for introducing *public* agencies to provide commercial agri-support services is different in the two cases.

Where the tendency toward monopoly is the situation to be remedied, it may make little difference whether the new additional agency is public or a competing private agency. The competing private agency can be another private firm or a truly independent and non-official cooperative society. The goal to be sought is *for farmers to have effective options,* preferably in each farming locality, in dealing with sellers of farm inputs, buyers of farm products and suppliers of farm credit.

In general, farmers do not trust merchants and lenders, whether these are private or public. Where any merchant or lender, whether private or public, has a local monopoly such trust is lowest. What farmers need is a choice among different suppliers of marketing or credit services in their own locality.

Where the objective is to assure that adequate commercial agri-support services are available to small farmers, and not just to large ones, the problem is different. Here one must deal with the hard fact that it is more expensive to provide equal facilities to small than to large farmers (as it is to serve regions where commercial agriculture is just getting started). Credit, particularly, is more expensive to dispense and to recover when it consists of a large number of quite small loans. Historically, this problem has been tackled in three ways. One is the Comilla pattern of making loans only to local cooperative societies, the members of which are jointly responsible for distributing the credit to individual members and for repaying the loan. The second is to combine the dispensing of credit with other (usually extension) activities in order to reduce the overhead charges for both. The third is via a public credit agency with its administrative costs borne by the government in order that borrowers of small amounts may be adequately served.

Whether commercial agri-support services are privately or publicly operated, however, there are essential public activities with

140

respect to them that need to be provided. Insofar as commercial agri-support services are public, the public responsibility is administrative. Insofar as they are privately managed, public arrangements must still be made to regulate them, curbing monopoly tendencies and setting standards for quality.

Appendix B

"AGRICULTURAL DEVELOPMENT OFFICERS"

On page 68 reference was made to the participation of "representatives of field agricultural development officers" in the consultative deliberations of the Office of Planning. In this context, "field agricultural development officers" may mean persons holding any one of several different positions.

Some countries have persons officially designated as "agricultural development officers." They may or may not have line administrative authority over the personnel of all ministry of agriculture personnel operating in a district.[42] Whether they have line authority or not they need to perform two functions related to agricultural planning. One is to keep assessing and reassessing the changing potential for growth in agricultural production of different parts of each farming district and feeding these assessments, and their own recommendations as to what programs the ministry should mount, strengthen, or withdraw in that district

---

[42] Issues bearing on the decisions as to whether or not they should be "line" administrators are discussed in *Creating a Progressive Rural Structure, op. cit.,* especially Chapter 3.

in the following year, into the planning procedures of the ministry. Their other function is to monitor and report on performance of all elements of the ministry's program within the district.

If agricultural development officers are *not* line officers, in charge of directing all ministry activities in the district, they can concentrate solely on these two functions. If they *are* line officers, then each of them may need a full-time assistant to concentrate on these assessing and monitoring functions.

Appropriate representatives of field agricultural officials need to be involved in the planning process even if a country does not have any persons officially designated as "agricultural development officers." In that case, it may be better not to have all such representatives come from the same agency or agricultural service but to select individuals who personally have a broad understanding of agricultural development and an aptitude for committee consultations, whatever the specialized service with which each is connected.

Appendix C

"INVESTMENT" AND "CURRENT OUTLAYS"

An excerpt from Edward S. Mason, *On the Appropriate Size of a Development Program,* Harvard Center for International Affairs, Occasional Papers, No. 8, August 1964, pp. 19-22. Reprinted by permission.

Public development expenditures, as pointed out earlier, usually include, in addition to capital investment, certain types of current outlays. But the distinction between development and ordinary government expenditures is not very clear, nor is it made in the same way in different development plans. The justification for treating certain expenditures as developmental is, presumably, that they bear a relation to future output similar to that of capital investment. And certainly it is clear by now that traditional distinctions between capital formation and consumption do not serve very effectively either the analysis of growth or development planning. Kuznets makes this point effectively.

"If by capital formation we mean the use of any current resources that add to future output, even on a per capita or per worker basis, many of the categories now treated under flow of goods to ultimate consumers should be included under capital. Certainly significant fractions of outlays in education and training, travel and recreation, improvement of health and even outlays on living, insofar as they contribute to the greater productivity of the population, are among these categories. Perhaps this new dividing line cannot be drawn with any assurance. But it does seem that if capital is what capital does—contributes to increased productivity—much of what is now classified under consumer outlay in advanced economic societies rightly belongs under capital."[13]

A sizable body of literature has in recent years been devoted to a demonstration that growth rates in advanced economies can be only fractionally explained by measurable increases in "conventional" inputs. The "unconventional" inputs alleged to explain the other—and larger—fraction are variously described as technological improvement, human-resource development, institutional and organizational changes, etc. The financial counterpart of these inputs would appear to be mainly current outlays rather than capital investment. Despite heroic efforts by Denison and others to trace various types of current outlays through to increases in output, it must be said that our notions concerning which outlays yield current consumption and which yield future output are still imprecise.[14] Yet the central conception is fairly clear. If an outlay can be expected to produce an increment of output over a succession of future periods—to yield, i.e., a rate of return—it is presumably entitled to be called a development expenditure whether or not it can be described as capital formation.

For certain types of current expenditure no serious difficulties are encountered. In the development program proposed by

---

[13] Simon Kuznets, "Toward a Theory of Economic Growth," in R. Lekachman (ed.), *National Policy for Economic Welfare at Home and Abroad* (New York, 1955), p. 40.

[14] Edward F. Denison, *The Sources of Economic Growth in the United States and the Alternatives Before Us* (New York, 1962).

the International Bank Survey Mission for Uganda it was recommended that £5 million of Marketing Board funds be used
for current expenditures to promote agricultural productivity.
These expenditures were to be mainly devoted to subsidizing
sprays and spraying equipment and to paying the salaries of
officials to instruct in their use. The rationale of this recommendation was that the expected increase in productivity generated by expenditures over a two- or three-year period would
establish a type of behavior that could be expected to yield a
"perpetual" rate of return.[15] At the same time, it was urged on
the Survey Mission that increased expenditure on the police
should also be included in the development program because
an improved standard of law and order could make a positive
contribution to the productiveness of the economy. If a distinction relevant to development is to be made between these
two types of expenditures, it can only be along the line that
one produces benefits that mainly accrue in the future while
the other produces current benefits that will disappear with a
reduction or elimination of the expenditure in question.[16]

It is, however, difficult if not impossible clearly to distinguish
developmental from non-developmental expenditures on this
basis or probably on any other. Definitions of developmental
expenditures differ not only among countries but in the same
country between plans.[17] Perhaps it is relatively unimportant
whether or not a particular type of expenditure is called devel-

---

[15] Later observations in Uganda suggest that these expenditures, so far as cotton
is concerned, failed to yield the expected increase in productivity. It appears to be
the case in Uganda that returns to effort in the cultivation of other crops may be
sufficiently favorable to discourage the concentration needed to accomplish large
productivity increases in cotton.

[16] Cf. D. Usher, "The Concept of Development Expenditure," *Indian Economic
Journal* (Apr., 1963).

[17] "The concept of development expenditure used in the Second Plan differs in
some significant aspects from that used in the First Plan. D. E., as defined in the
First Plan, covered not only gross fixed investment, but also the recurring and non-
recurring costs of all the new schemes in the fields of education, health, Village
Aid and other social services. Development expenditure, as the term has been used
in the Second Plan, does not include the recurring costs of schemes in the public
sector, except recurring expenditures in popularizing, distributing and subsidizing

opmental. But mistakes in policy can certainly arise from a failure to recognize the appropriate role for these different kinds of government outlays: as, for example, misguided attempts to economize on non-development expenditures in order to increase development outlays. The distinction is not between important and unimportant outlays but between those yielding current and those yielding future returns. An increase in public investment at the expense of outlays on police or revenue collection is not necessarily a "good thing." Nor is it necessarily a good thing to attempt to create the illusion of a large development program by including in proposed development expenditures outlays better classified as current outlays of government. Fiscal wisdom perhaps suggests a certain conservatism in the definition of development expenditures and stability in expenditure classification once it is achieved.

It remains true, nevertheless, that investment in fixed capital and inventories excludes a type of expenditure that does the same thing that capital investment is supposed to do—i.e., yield a future return—and there are persuasive arguments for including these in any discussion of the appropriate size of a development program.

---

fertilizers; salaries of agricultural extension workers engaged in schemes specifically included in the Plan; Village Aid and Community Development Schemes; technical, industrial, agricultural, and social research related to specific Plan schemes; family planning; scholarships and malarial control. All other recurring costs are classified as non-developmental." *The Second Five-Year Plan of Pakistan (1960-65)* (Karachi: Planning Commission, 1960), p. 10.

Appendix D

PLANNING FOR AGRICULTURAL DEVELOPMENT

Professor John W. Mellor, Cornell University

Excerpts from a paper presented at the Eighth World Conference of the Society for International Development, New York, 1966. Reprinted by permission.

The essence of planning for developing agriculture is to (1) determine the kinds of institutions needed for creating technological change, (2) determine the optimal organization of these institutions, (3) determine the quantity of inputs needed both for these institutions and to complement the application of technology on farms.

Traditional planning techniques place major attention on allocations of physical inputs. [But] in developing an experiment station system, or an extension system, or a fertilizer distribution system the quantities of money, or of manpower and other physical resources allocated are less important in determining their effectiveness and output than the way they are organized.

Research institutions, which are such prime prerequisites of technological change in agriculture perhaps illustrate this point best. Many nations make large expenditures on research in the agricultural sciences. Few get productive results. The difference lies with the administrative structure of experiment stations, the means used for coordination of research at different stations, the nature of the contact between experiment stations and operating agriculture, the kinds of persons hired and the incentives given them, and many other factors. Effective agricultural development planning must place emphasis on these considerations.

Appendix E

AGRICULTURAL TARGETS

The setting of "targets" to be achieved is a customary part of agricultural planning. These are usually production targets for specific commodities. But it is implicit in the discussion of this book that commodity targets are inappropriate for agricultural planning during the period when creating a modern agriculture is the primary objective.

During that period, primary emphasis must be on creating the structure of a modern agriculture, district by district, over as much of the country as that may be economic. Consequently, the targets set in a plan should be targets with respect to each of the major elements of a modern agriculture, and different kinds of targets are appropriate for different ones of those elements.

For example, agricultural research is a basic element in the structure of a modern agriculture. In order to estimate the total investment that should be made in research, over time, requires an estimate of the nature and size of the agricultural research system that the country will need in view of its size, heterogeneity, and resource endowment. Against that estimate of total need, targets can be set for phased accomplishments toward that goal, given the constraints of trained manpower, necessary gestation periods, and the demands of other activities on the same resources.

Creating a Progressive Rural Structure is amenable to similar analysis. The starting point here is the absolute area now classified as having an immediate agricultural growth potential because it is only in such regions that investment in a Progressive Rural Structure is economic for the time being. Given the total area of present IGP lands, and making a judgment about the time period over which the country is willing to phase its achievement of a Progressive Rural Structure in its IGP areas, targets can then be set in terms of land area to be covered each year by a Progressive Rural Structure. These targets will be limited by the physical and administrative capacity to create the additional facilities needed, on the one hand, and by constraints of resource availability, on the other.

Land development targets are subject to other but similar restraints. The classification of the agricultural lands of a country as to growth potential is a necessary preliminary step here also. Land development is particularly important for FGP areas because land development and/or appropriate research are the most important activities that can lift FGP areas into the IGP category. The major constraints will be technical feasibility, cost per acre improved, and the availability of funds for expenditure. This latter constraint is less binding than in the case of most other activities because IBRD or other external loans are more readily available (and appropriate) for land development than for many other activities. Targets of accomplishment will be in terms of acreages of land to be irrigated, drained, or otherwise developed.

Targets are quite different in the case of allocations for affecting farmers' production incentives. Incentives that can be manipulated through subsidies, taxation, price policies, etc., are no substitute for such basic elements of a modern agriculture as research, a Progressive Rural Structure, and land development. They can only affect the way in which farmers respond to the

151

opportunities that those more basic elements make possible. Consequently the targets that can be set for activities to affect production incentives are in terms of production increases (or decreases) of particular farm commodities that it is considered desirable to achieve or in terms of projected increases of average farm incomes or of desired changes in income distribution.

Targets should take still another form in the case of activities to manufacture or import farm inputs. Here, they should be related primarily to projections of near future demands for them as indicated partly by recent past trends and partly by the rate at which a Progressive Rural Structure is being made available to additional land areas. They should *not* be targets calculated to meet the input needs of particular commodity targets.

Targets with respect to training agricultural technicians should be a *resultant* of plans for all other types of activities, taking into account the likelihood that there will be more and more opportunities for lucrative private employment for persons with certain types of agricultural training in various commercial agri-support activities, as well as in farm management as farming becomes more profitable.

Thus, in the form of agricultural planning being proposed here *production* planning—setting production targets for specific farm commodities—becomes quite secondary. Such planning is more pertinent to the period *after* the structure of a modern agriculture has been largely achieved. To attempt it earlier can absorb much planning ability that could better be expended on more detailed planning for each of the elements of creating a modern agriculture. It can distract attention from more urgent planning tasks related specifically to creating the elements of a modern agriculture.

Nevertheless, even within the period we are discussing it will usually be considered desirable to try to achieve increases in the production of certain commodities. The best way to meet such needs is within planning: (1) with respect to farmers' production incentives; (2) types of research to be given priority; and (3) regions to receive first attention with respect both to land development and expansion of a Progressive Rural Structure. Appropriate action at those points can achieve the greatest increase in the production of selected farm commodities that is possible in any case and will avoid the distorting effects of letting production targets dominate the agricultural planning process.

Appendix F

"AN INSTITUTIONAL APPROACH TO DEVELOPMENT PLANNING"

Excerpts from Raanan Weitz, *From Peasant to Farmer: A Revolutionary Strategy for Development* (New York: Columbia University Press, 1971), chapt. 12. Reprinted by permission.

Developing nations are particularly enthusiastic about development planning, and most of them have some sort of program, at least on paper. The planning fashion is rampant, but it has not yet justified itself in practical results. Why is this so?

The main reason is the indiscriminate application by the developing countries of planning procedures evolved and used in the advanced countries. These procedures are based to a large extent on the use of highly sophisticated mathematical models and various analytical techniques whose validity depends on two basic assumptions. The first assumption is that it is possible to formulate the most effective measures for changing situation 'A' in the present to situation 'B' in the future while still at situation 'A'. This approach may be compared to the launching of a ballistic missile, for which all the necessary data must be obtained and all the arrangements made in advance, so that once the ballistic missile is launched, it will hit the target without further intervention. Implicit in this approach is the assumption that situation 'B' is both realistic and desirable and will continue to be so for the duration of the operation.

The second assumption is that both the present situation 'A' and the target situation 'B' can be represented in mathematical terms.

Both of the assumptions on which these models are based render them unsuitable for practical use in the developing countries, and particularly in their rural areas. The first one does not take into consideration that a great number of factors cannot be foreseen and assessed in advance, as they appear only during the transition from situation 'A' to situation 'B'. Furthermore, the present planning models are based to a large extent on forecasts derived from extrapolation of past trends. As such they are incapable of taking into account the nature and impact of future technological innovations, which have a major influence on the pace of development.

The second assumption fails to take into account that many important factors, especially those that relate to the social and organizational spheres, do not lend themselves to mathematical representation and cannot be fitted to equations. Attributing quantitative values to these factors distorts their meaning. Indeed, it is generally considered that the major difficulty in the practical application of these models is the assignment of relative values or weights to the different factors involved. This is true for all countries and for all levels of development, but is especially true in traditional societies with subsistence economies, where the basic information concerning the economic structure and modes of behavior is still missing.

Apart from the above limitations inherent in the nature of mathematical models, there is a much more fundamental consideration that renders the planning procedures of the advanced countries inapplicable for the less developed ones. These procedures were developed for economies with mature,

155

efficient, and highly flexible production systems. Therefore, they assume a high mobility for all factors of production and that the producers are both willing and capable of responding to policy measures. Such policies include, in particular, monetary and fiscal measures regarding, for example, taxes, subsidies, and price regulation.

This approach is not effective in dealing with the conditions of developing countries. Take, for example, the organization of agricultural production, which is of prime importance in these countries. It is reasonably easy to calculate the quantity and composition of agricultural commodities that would be required to satisfy demand. The difficulty lies in the inability of the agricultural producers to respond to this demand. The lack of response derives from a number of reasons, the most important being defective institutional arrangements that prevent the producers from introducing the necessary changes in the utilization of resources.

The planning methods and policies that seem to be effective in Western countries are therefore unsuitable for the needs of the developing countries. The goals are different, as are the institutional arrangements on which these methods are based. What the developing countries need is, first and foremost, institutional reform, to lay the foundations for an effective supply system. Without prior institutional adjustments, the desired results will not be attained, because what is needed is to change the 'way of doing things'—the traditional structure and patterns of behavior.

Nor are the planning procedures of the communist countries capable of solving the problem, although on first examination they might seem to be highly suitable. It is true that centralized planning is designed to improve the exploitation of resources by specifying in detail their particular utilization. There is, however, a total disregard of the human element and its role in development. No account is taken of the need to motivate the people and induce them to use the resources available to them in the most efficient manner.

For the purpose of implementing the rural development program outlined in this book, an entirely new approach to planning is needed. Its most important attributes should be flexibility, comprehensiveness, and, above all, a proper approach to the human element involved in the process of development. New forms of community organization, of the supporting system, and of various social institutions provide the base for the attainment of development goals—an increase in total production and in the standards of living of the population. Since institutional change forms the basis of this program, the planning method required for its realization is called 'institutional planning.'

Rural development is the end result of interactions between the various institutional reforms, economic policies, and technical programs. For example, to increase total output from the individual farm, it is necessary to introduce technological innovations, to train the farmer in their use, to provide him with sufficient resources, and to create the necessary infrastructure of service facilities for supply and marketing. Ultimately, however, it is the response of individual producers to these measures that determines the success or failure of the development plan.

The planning method required to accomplish the institutional changes, which form the essence of development planning, must therefore be geared, first and foremost, toward the people, their potentialities, and their motivations. It is not sufficient to determine the environmental conditions, to select the best possible way of utilizing material resources, and to expect the people to follow the chosen way of action. The emphasis should be placed on the motives of the people—sometimes known, sometimes only guessed at. It is necessary to provoke their interest, give expression to their inner drives and aspirations, and help them toward the creation of a new institutional structure capable of achieving the aims of development. The rationale of institutional planning is that development plans, and particularly programs for agricultural and rural development, must

157

be adapted to the needs of man, who is their focus and central object.

Although this approach is gaining wide recognition, it has not yet been reflected in planning methods used to date. While financial, economic, and technical measures are extremely important in any effort to increase production, in the absence of active participation by the people concerned, the effect of these measures will be relatively small. The individual producer should be regarded as a human being, not as another factor of production; plans should be coordinated with the desires and abilities of the population for whom they are designed.

Apart from its emphasis on the human element and on institution-building, the proposed method and planning must fulfill two additional requirements.

First, it must be integrative, that is, it must be capable of assessing the significance of all the factors affecting the development process.

Second, flexibility must be an essential part of institutional planning. What this implies is that a development plan must be able to absorb all changes of either a quantitative or qualitative nature in a factor or group of interrelated factors that may occur during the time it is being implemented.

To sum up, the nature and number of the factors that affect a development program and their interdependencies comprise an awesome complex. It is a complex that crosses the lines between disciplines, reaches beyond the quantifiable, and does not even remain entirely within the realm of objective reasoning. But it is only by attempting to grasp the meaning of the various factors affecting the development process and their dynamic relationships that a sound base for development planning may be constructed. This will not be achieved by the use of dry figures alone. Direct contact with reality is an essential ingredient of effective planning and is a fundamental tenet of the institutional approach to development.

BIBLIOGRAPHY

Hayami, Y., and Ruttan, V. W. *Agricultural Development: An International Perspective*. Baltimore: Johns Hopkins University Press, 1971.

Johnson, E. A. J. *The Organization of Space in Developing Countries*. Cambridge, Mass.: Harvard University Press, 1970.

Joint Commission on Rural Reconstruction. "Agricultural Development and Its Contribution to Economic Growth on Taiwan." *Economic Digest*, Series No. 17, Taipei (April 1966).

Mellor, John W. "Agricultural Policies for Accelerating Progress." Paper presented at the Eighth World Conference of the Society for International Development, New York, March 1966.

Millikan, Max F. "Relationship Between Agricultural and Economic Development." Paper presented at the CENTO Conference on National and Regional Agricultural Development Policy, Istanbul, Sept. 1967.

Mosher, A. T. "Administrative Experimentation as a Way of Life for Developmental Programs." *International Development Review*, Vol. IX, No. 2 (June 1967), pp. 38-41.

————. *Creating a Progressive Rural Structure*. New York: Agricultural Development Council, 1969.

Myrdal, Gunnar. *Asian Drama*. Vol. III, Appendix 3. New York: Pantheon, 1968.

Penny, D. H. "The Transition from Subsistence to Commercial Family Farming in North Sumatra." Unpublished Ph.D. dissertation, Cornell University, 1964.

159

Schultz, T. W. *Transforming Traditional Agriculture*. New Haven: Yale University Press, 1966.

Stolper, Wolfgang F. *Planning Without Facts: Lessons in Resource Allocation from Nigeria's Development*. Cambridge, Mass.: Harvard University Press, 1966.

U.S. Office of Economic Opportunity. *PERT for CAA Planning: A Programmed Course of Instruction in PERT*. OEO Training Manual 6321-1. 2 vols. Washington, D.C.: Executive Office of the President, 1969.

Waterston, Albert. *Development Planning: Lessons of Experience*. Baltimore: Johns Hopkins University Press, 1965.

————. "Sector Programming." Washington, D.C.: International Bank for Reconstruction and Development, n.d. (Mimeographed.)

The World Food Problem: A Report of the President's Science Advisory Committee. Vol. I, pp. 60-73. Vol. II, pp. 504-35. Washington, D.C.: The White House, May 1967.

OTHER SUGGESTED READINGS

Abraham, William I. *Annual Budgeting and Development Planning*. Planning Methods Series No. 1, Center for Development Planning. Washington, D.C.: National Planning Association, 1965.

Grasberg, Eugene. "Development Project Formats: A Design for Maximum Information." *Development Digest*, Vol. V, No. 2 (July 1967).

Hammond, Richard J. "Convention and Limitation in Benefit-Cost Analysis." Food Research Institute Papers No. 2-66. Stanford, Calif.: Food Research Institute, 1966.

Rivkin, Malcolm D. "Let's Think Small for Development." *International Development Review*, Vol. V, No. 1 (March 1963), pp. 24-28.

Seers, Dudley. "The Meaning of Development." Presidential Address to the Eleventh World Conference of the Society for International Development, 1969. Reprinted by the Agricultural Development Council, New York, September 1970.

United Nations. Economic Commission for Latin America. Dept. of Economic and Social Affairs, Fiscal and Financial Branch. *A Manual for Programme and Performance Budgeting (Draft)*. (E/CN.12/BRW. 2/L.5), 1962.

Waterston, Albert. "An Operational Approach to Development Planning." Washington, D.C.: International Bank for Reconstruction and Development, n.d. (Mimeographed.)

_____. "What Do We Know About Planning." *International Development Review*, Vol. VII, No. 4 (December 1965), pp. 2-10.

Weitz, Raanan. *From Peasant to Farmer: A Revolutionary Strategy for Development*. New York: Columbia University Press, 1971.

Wharton, Clifton R., Jr. "The Infrastructure of Agricultural Growth." Chapter 4 of *Agricultural Development and Economic Growth*. Edited by H. M. Southworth and B. F. Johnston. Ithaca, N. Y.: Cornell University Press, 1967.

————. "Strategies for Rural Development." New York: Agricultural Development Council, 1966. (Mimeographed.)